Answer Book

6

Heinemann Educational Publishers
Halley Court, Jordan Hill, Oxford, OX2 8EJ
a division of Harcourt Education Ltd
www.heinemann.co.uk

Heinemann is a registered trademark of Harcourt Education Ltd

First published 2003

06 05 04 03
10, 9, 8, 7, 6, 5, 4, 3, 2, 1

ISBN 0 435 20785 7

Cover illustration by Dave Cockburn
Designed by Tech-Set
Printed in Great Britain by Ashford Colour Press, Gosport, Hants

Contents

PUPIL BOOK

PB ■ 1

1
  a 300, 3000
  b 4200, 42 000
  c 85 400, 854 000
  d 70 100, 701 000
  e 240, 2400
  f 631, 6310
  g 47·2, 472
  h 300·4, 3004

2
  a 65·32, 6·532
  b 3·94, 0·394
  c 0·839, 0·083 9
  d 0·670 2, 0·067 02
  e 0·05, 0·005
  f 0·001, 0·000 1
  g 0·031, 0·003 1
  h 0·070 4, 0·007 04

3
  a six hundred and eighty thousand seven hundred and twenty
  b six hundred and eighty thousand seven hundred and twenty point four
  c six thousand eight hundred and seven point two zero four
  d six million eight hundred and seven thousand two hundred and four
  e sixty-eight thousand and seventy-two point zero four
  f six hundred and eighty point seven two zero four

4
  a 6·3
  b 8
  c 8·45
  d 3·86
  e 10

5
  a 8·59
  b 4·06
  c 2·99
  d 8·09
  e 9

PB ■ 2

1
  a $<$
  b $<$
  c $<$
  d $>$
  e $>$
  f $<$

2 Any number that is
  a greater than 7·5 and less than 8·2
  b greater than 6·1 and less than 6·9
  c greater than 8·03 and less than 8·05
  d greater than 5·7 and less than 5·8
  e greater than 4 and less than 4·1
  f greater than 6·13 and less than 6·14

3 Amount lifted:
Jo 1·567 kg
Lennox 1576 g
Louise 1·639 kg
Dan 1885 g
Ed 1904 g

Height jumped:
Ed 0·89 m
Dan 98 cm
Lennox 1·06 m
Louise 116 cm
Jo 1·17 m

Money collected:
Louise 94p
Lennox £0·96
Dan 207p

Ed £2·70
Jo £3·46

4 a 0·684
  b Smallest possible difference is
    0·014 from a pair such as 0·612
    and 0·598.

❓ Largest possible difference is 0·864
  from 0·987 and 0·123.

PB ■ 3

1 330
  4070
  5970
  18 350

2 400
  5800
  7000
  28 700

3 3000
  37 000
  41 000
  77 000

4 a 300 g, 320 g
  b 200 g, 170 g
  c 600 g, 570 g

5
  a 200 cm
  b 220 cm
  c 219 cm
  d 218·7 cm
  e 2·19 m
  f 2 m

PB ■ 4

1 a ⁻9, ⁻6, ⁻2, 1, 3
  b ⁻8, ⁻5, ⁻2.4, 4·2, 7
  c ⁻24, ⁻17, ⁻11, 13, 15
  d ⁻45, ⁻18·6, ⁻18·3, 0, 27

2 a Any 3 from the following pairs:
    ⁻5 and ⁻3,
    ⁻6 and ⁻2,
    ⁻7 and ⁻1,
    ⁻8 and 0,
    ⁻9 and 1,
    ⁻10 and 2
  b Any 3 from the following pairs:
    ⁻7 and ⁻5,
    ⁻8 and ⁻4,
    ⁻9 and ⁻3,
    ⁻10 and ⁻2
  c Any 3 from the following pairs:
    ⁻2 and 0,
    ⁻3 and 1,
    ⁻4 and 2,
    ⁻5 and 3,
    ⁻6 and 4,
    ⁻7 and 5,
    ⁻8 and 6,
    ⁻9 and 7,
    ⁻10 and 8

PB ■ 5

1 a 43, 43
  b 19, 19
  c ⁻26, ⁻26
  d 11, 11

2 a 3, 3
  b ⁻14, ⁻14
  c ⁻120, ⁻120
  d ⁻94, ⁻94

3 a 0·272 727
  b 3·666 666
  c 0·272 727
  d 3·666 666
  e 0·272 727
  f 3·666 666

4 a $\dfrac{3·1 - 1·3}{3·1 + 1·3} = 0·409\,090\,9$

$\dfrac{3·1 + 1·3}{3·1 - 1·3} = 2·444\,444$

$$b \quad \frac{6 \cdot 2 - 2 \cdot 6}{6 \cdot 2 + 2 \cdot 6} = 0 \cdot 409\ 090\ 9$$

$$\frac{6 \cdot 2 + 2 \cdot 6}{6 \cdot 2 - 2 \cdot 6} = 2 \cdot 444\ 444$$

$$\frac{9 \cdot 3 - 3 \cdot 9}{9 \cdot 3 + 3 \cdot 9} = 0 \cdot 409\ 090\ 9$$

$$\frac{9 \cdot 3 + 3 \cdot 9}{9 \cdot 3 - 3 \cdot 9} = 2 \cdot 444\ 444$$

PB ■ 6

1 **a** 70
 b 231
 c 210
 d 36
 e 225
 f 900

2 **a** $6 = 2 \times 3$

 b $9 = 3^2$

 c $30 = 5 \times 2 \times 3$

 d $36 = 2^2 \times 3^2$

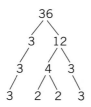

 e $60 = 2^2 \times 3 \times 5$

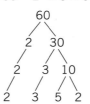

3 $24 = 2^3 \times 3$
 4 possible factor trees based on:
 2×12, 3×8 and 4×6
 $36 = 2^2 \times 3^2$
 6 possible factor trees based on:
 2×18, 3×12, 4×9 and 6×6
 $48 = 2^4 \times 3$
 9 possible factor trees based on:
 2×24, 3×16, 4×12 and 6×8
 $60 = 2^2 \times 3 \times 5$
 9 possible factor trees based on:
 2×30, 3×20, 4×15, 5×12
 and 6×10
 $72 = 2^3 \times 3^2$
 15 possible factor trees based on:
 2×36, 3×24, 4×18, 6×12
 and 8×9

PB ■ 7

1 **a** 2933   5024
 b 293   502
 c 6   8
 d $293 - 6 = 287$ $502 - 8 = 494$
 e $28 - 14 = 14$ $49 - 8 = 41$
   $1 - 8 = {}^-7$ $4 - 2 = 2$
 f 2933 is divisible by 7
 g 5024 is not divisible by 7
   $2933 \div 7 = 419$
   $5024 \div 7 = 717 \cdot 71$

2 **a** 40 is divisible by:
   1 and 40
   2 and 20
   4 and 10
   5 and 8

41 is divisible by:
1 and 41

42 is divisible by:
1 and 42
2 and 21
3 and 14
6 and 7

43 is divisible by:
1 and 43

44 is divisible by:
1 and 44
2 and 22
4 and 11

45 is divisible by:
1 and 45
3 and 15
5 and 9

46 is divisible by:
1 and 46
2 and 23

47 is divisible by:
1 and 47

48 is divisible by:
1 and 48
2 and 24
3 and 16
4 and 12
6 and 8

49 is divisible by:
1 and 49
7 and 7

50 is divisible by:
1 and 50
2 and 25
5 and 10

? Child's own lists of divisors for numbers between 100 and 124.

PB ■ 8
1 *a* 13
   b 17
   c 61

d 101
e 34
f 10
g 68
h 74
i 202

2 *a* 64
   b 8
   c 11
   d 12
   e 21
   f 45
   g 28
   h 3
   i 63

3 *a* $7^2 - 5^2 = 24$
      $(7 + 5) \times (7 - 5) = 12 \times 2$
      $= 24$
   b $10^2 - 3^2 = 91$
      $(10 + 3) \times (10 - 3)$
      $= 13 \times 7 = 91$
   c $15^2 - 11^2 = 104$
      $(15 + 11) \times (15 - 11)$
      $= 26 \times 4 = 104$
   d $21^2 - 19^2 = 80$
      $(21 + 19) \times (21 - 19)$
      $= 40 \times 2 = 80$
      Each pair of answers is the same.

4 *a* When divided by 3, the square numbers will only have a remainder of 0 or 1.
      $1^2 \div 3 = 0$ r 1
      $2^2 \div 3 = 1$ r 1
      $3^2 \div 3 = 3$
      $4^2 \div 3 = 5$ r 1
      $5^2 \div 3 = 8$ r 1
      $6^2 \div 3 = 12$
      $7^2 \div 3 = 16$ r 1
      $8^2 \div 3 = 21$ r 1
      $9^2 \div 3 = 27$
      $10^2 \div 3 = 33$ r 1
      $11^2 \div 3 = 40$ r 1

$12^2 \div 3 = 48$
$13^2 \div 3 = 56 \text{ r } 1$
$14^2 \div 3 = 65 \text{ r } 1$
$15^2 \div 3 = 75$
b $16^2 \div 3 = 85 \text{ r } 1$

PB ■ 9

1 $4^2 \times 4^2 \times 4^2 \times 4^2$ has the greatest value:
$2^2 \times 2^2 \times 2^2 \times 2^2 \times 2^2 \times 2^2 = 4096$
$3^2 \times 3^2 \times 3^2 \times 3^2 \times 3^2 = 59\,049$
$4^2 \times 4^2 \times 4^2 \times 4^2 = 65\,536$
$5^2 \times 5^2 \times 5^2 = 15\,625$
$6^2 \times 6^2 = 1296$

2 $2 = 2^1$
$4 = 2^2$
$8 \, (= 2^3)$
$16 \, (= 2^4)$
$32 \, (= 2^5)$
$64 \, (= 2^6)$

3 $3^2 = 9$
$33^2 = 1089$
$333^2 = 110\,889$
$3333^2 = 11\,108\,889$
$33\,333^2 = 1\,111\,088\,889$

? $9^2 = 81$
$99^2 = 9801$
$999^2 = 998\,001$
$9999^2 = 99\,980\,001$
$99\,999^2 = 9\,999\,800\,001$

PB ■ 10

1 a 49
   b 144
   c 400
   d 625
   e 289

2 a Rashid appears to have found a repeating pattern: 1, 8, 9, 1, 8, 9 … in the digital roots.

b $7 \times 7 \times 7 = 343$
$\downarrow$
1
$8 \times 8 \times 8 = 512$
$\downarrow$
8
$9 \times 9 \times 9 = 729$
$\downarrow$
9
$10 \times 10 \times 10 = 1000$
$\downarrow$
1
$11 \times 11 \times 11 = 1331$
$\downarrow$
8
$12 \times 12 \times 12 = 1728$
$\downarrow$
9
$13 \times 13 \times 13 = 2197$
$\downarrow$
1
$14 \times 14 \times 14 = 2744$
$\downarrow$
8
$15 \times 15 \times 15 = 3375$
$\downarrow$
9
$16 \times 16 \times 16 = 4096$
$\downarrow$
1
$17 \times 17 \times 17 = 4913$
$\downarrow$
8
$18 \times 18 \times 18 = 5832$
$\downarrow$
9
$19 \times 19 \times 19 = 6859$
$\downarrow$
1
$20 \times 20 \times 20 = 8000$
$\downarrow$
8

Rashid is correct.

(?) There is a repeating pattern in the units digits of the numbers:
1, 8, 7, 4, 5, 6, 3, 2, 9, 0, 1, 8, 7, 4, 5, 6, 3, 2, 9, 0

PB ■ 11

1 a $\sqrt{4} \times \sqrt{100} = 20$
$\sqrt{400} = 20$
b $\sqrt{9} \times \sqrt{100} = 30$
$\sqrt{900} = 30$
c $\sqrt{16} \times \sqrt{100} = 40$
$\sqrt{1600} = 40$
d 200
e 300
f 400

2 a 81, 9
b 1444, 38
The square root of the square is the original number because finding the square and square root are inverse operations.

3 a 2·645 751 3, 7
b 5·567 764 4, 31
The square of the square root is the original number because square and square root are inverse operations.

PB ■ 12

1 a $<$
b $<$
c $<$
d $<$
e $>$
f $>$
g $<$
h $>$
i $<$
j $<$
k $>$
l $<$

2 a $\frac{2}{3}, \frac{3}{4}, \frac{5}{6}$
b $1\frac{1}{5}, 1\frac{3}{10}, 1\frac{3}{4}$
c $2\frac{1}{10}, 2\frac{2}{5}, 2\frac{1}{2}$
d $\frac{3}{4}, \frac{7}{9}, 1\frac{3}{3}, 2\frac{1}{5}, 2\frac{2}{7}$

3 a Possible answers include any 3 from:
$\frac{3}{11}, \frac{6}{22}, \frac{9}{33}, \frac{12}{44} \cdots$
$\frac{2}{7}, \frac{4}{14}, \frac{6}{21}, \frac{8}{28} \cdots$
$\frac{1}{3}, \frac{2}{6}, \frac{3}{9}, \frac{4}{12}, \frac{5}{15} \cdots$
$\frac{3}{8}, \frac{6}{16}, \frac{9}{24}, \frac{12}{32} \cdots$
$\frac{2}{5}, \frac{4}{10}, \frac{6}{15}, \frac{8}{20} \cdots$
$\frac{3}{7}, \frac{6}{14}, \frac{9}{21}, \frac{12}{28} \cdots$
$\frac{4}{9}, \frac{8}{18}, \frac{12}{27}, \frac{16}{36} \cdots$

b Possible answers include any 3 from:
$\frac{3}{8}, \frac{6}{16}, \frac{9}{24}, \frac{12}{32} \cdots$
$\frac{2}{5}, \frac{4}{10}, \frac{6}{15}, \frac{8}{20} \cdots$
$\frac{3}{7}, \frac{6}{14}, \frac{9}{21}, \frac{12}{28} \cdots$
$\frac{4}{9}, \frac{8}{18}, \frac{12}{27}, \frac{16}{36} \cdots$

c Possible answers include any 3 from:
$\frac{3}{14}, \frac{6}{28}, \frac{9}{42}, \frac{12}{56} \cdots$
$\frac{2}{9}, \frac{4}{18}, \frac{6}{27}, \frac{8}{36} \cdots$
$\frac{3}{13}, \frac{6}{26}, \frac{9}{39}, \frac{12}{52} \cdots$
$\frac{4}{17}, \frac{8}{34}, \frac{12}{51}, \frac{16}{68} \cdots$

d Possible answers include any 3 from:
$\frac{3}{8}, \frac{6}{16}, \frac{9}{24}, \frac{12}{32} \cdots$
$\frac{2}{5}, \frac{4}{10}, \frac{6}{15}, \frac{8}{20} \cdots$
$\frac{3}{7}, \frac{6}{14}, \frac{9}{21}, \frac{12}{28} \cdots$
$\frac{4}{9}, \frac{8}{18}, \frac{12}{27}, \frac{16}{36} \cdots$
$\frac{1}{2}, \frac{2}{4}, \frac{3}{6}, \frac{4}{8}, \frac{5}{10} \cdots$
$\frac{5}{9}, \frac{10}{18}, \frac{15}{27}, \frac{20}{36} \cdots$
$\frac{4}{7}, \frac{8}{14}, \frac{12}{21}, \frac{16}{28} \cdots$
$\frac{3}{5}, \frac{6}{10}, \frac{9}{15}, \frac{12}{20} \cdots$

e Possible answers include any 3 from:
$\frac{8}{13}, \frac{16}{26} \cdots$
$\frac{5}{8}, \frac{10}{16}, \frac{15}{24}, \frac{20}{32} \cdots$
$\frac{9}{14}, \frac{18}{28} \cdots$

$\frac{2}{3}, \frac{4}{6}, \frac{6}{9}, \frac{8}{12} \cdots$

$\frac{5}{7}, \frac{10}{14} \cdots$

$\frac{3}{4}, \frac{6}{8}, \frac{9}{12}, \frac{12}{16} \cdots$

$\frac{7}{9}, \frac{14}{18}, \frac{21}{27} \cdots$

f Possible answers include any 3 from:

$\frac{11}{13}, \frac{22}{26} \cdots$

$\frac{6}{7}, \frac{12}{14}, \frac{18}{21}, \frac{24}{28} \cdots$

$\frac{7}{8}, \frac{14}{16}, \frac{21}{24}, \frac{28}{32} \cdots$

$\frac{15}{17}, \frac{30}{34} \cdots$

$\frac{8}{9}, \frac{16}{18}, \frac{24}{27}, \frac{32}{36} \cdots$

$\frac{9}{10}, \frac{18}{20}, \frac{27}{30}, \frac{36}{40} \cdots$

$\frac{10}{11}, \frac{20}{22}, \frac{30}{33}, \frac{40}{44} \cdots$

4 Child's own investigation of fractions and their inverses.

PB ■ 13

1 a $\frac{48}{9} = 5\frac{1}{3}$

b $\frac{93}{6} = 15\frac{1}{2}$

c $\frac{22}{8} = 2\frac{3}{4}$

d $\frac{34}{4} = 8\frac{1}{2}$

e $\frac{68}{10} = 6\frac{4}{5}$

f $\frac{102}{14} = 7\frac{2}{7}$

2 a $4\frac{6}{9} = \frac{14}{3}$

b $7\frac{2}{4} = \frac{15}{2}$

c $3\frac{8}{12} = \frac{11}{3}$

d $6\frac{15}{20} = \frac{27}{4}$

e $9\frac{4}{6} = \frac{29}{3}$

f $8\frac{4}{10} = \frac{42}{5}$

3 a $\frac{1}{12}$

b $\frac{6}{7}$

c $\frac{2}{100}$

d $\frac{1}{22}$

e $\frac{2}{5}$ or $\frac{4}{10}$

f $\frac{9}{18}$ or $\frac{3}{6}$ or $\frac{1}{2}$

g $\frac{2}{13}$

4 a Child's constructed cuboid.

b 24

c 3 red, 9 blue, 4 green, 8 yellow

d 48

PB ■ 14

1 a $\frac{65}{100}$ or $\frac{13}{20}$

b $\frac{25}{1000}$ or $\frac{1}{40}$

c $\frac{27}{60}$ or $\frac{9}{20}$

d $\frac{500}{6000}$ or $\frac{1}{12}$

2 a $\frac{30}{360}$ or $\frac{1}{12}$

b $\frac{45}{360}$ or $\frac{1}{8}$

c $\frac{300}{360}$ or $\frac{5}{6}$

PB ■ 15

1 a $\frac{1}{3} = \frac{2}{6} = \frac{3}{9}$

$\frac{1}{8} = \frac{2}{16} = \frac{3}{24}$

$\frac{3}{4} = \frac{9}{12} = \frac{27}{36}$

$\frac{2}{5} = \frac{4}{10} = \frac{8}{20}$

b Answers include any 3 from each of:

$\frac{4}{12} = \frac{5}{15} = \frac{6}{18} = \frac{7}{21} = \frac{8}{24} = \frac{9}{27} = \frac{10}{30}$

$\cdots$

$\frac{4}{32} = \frac{5}{40} = \frac{6}{48} = \frac{7}{56} = \frac{8}{64} = \frac{9}{72} = \frac{10}{80}$

$\cdots$

$\frac{6}{8} = \frac{12}{16} = \frac{15}{20} = \frac{18}{24} = \frac{21}{28} = \frac{24}{32} = \frac{30}{40} \cdots$

$\frac{6}{15} = \frac{10}{25} = \frac{12}{30} = \frac{14}{35} = \frac{16}{40} = \frac{18}{45} = \frac{20}{50} \cdots$

c In the 1st set the numerators are multiples of 1 and the denominators are multiples of 3. The denominators are three times the numerators.

In the 2nd set the numerators are multiples of 1 and the denominators are multiples of 8. The denominators are eight times the numerators.

In the 3rd set the numerators are multiples of 3 and the denominators are multiples of 4.

If the numerator is the nth multiple of 3 then the denominator is the nth multiple of 4.

In the 4th set the numerators are multiples of 2 and the denominators are multiples of 5. If the numerator is the nth multiple of 2 then the denominator is the nth multiple of 5.

2 **a** Answers include any two from each of:

blue: $\frac{3}{5} = \frac{6}{10} = \frac{9}{15} = \frac{12}{20} = \frac{15}{25} = \frac{18}{30}$
$= \frac{21}{35} = \frac{24}{40} = \frac{27}{45} = \frac{30}{50} \cdots$
red: $\frac{2}{5} = \frac{4}{10} = \frac{6}{15} = \frac{8}{20} = \frac{10}{25} = \frac{12}{30}$
$= \frac{14}{35} = \frac{16}{40} = \frac{18}{45} = \frac{20}{50} \cdots$

b Answers include any two from each of:

blue: $\frac{1}{3} = \frac{2}{6} = \frac{3}{9} = \frac{4}{12} = \frac{5}{15} = \frac{6}{18} = \frac{7}{21}$
$= \frac{8}{24} = \frac{9}{27} = \frac{10}{30} \cdots$
red: $\frac{2}{3} = \frac{4}{6} = \frac{6}{9} = \frac{8}{12} = \frac{10}{15} = \frac{12}{18} = \frac{14}{21}$
$= \frac{16}{24} = \frac{18}{27} = \frac{20}{30} \cdots$

c Answers include any two from each of:

blue: $\frac{1}{4} = \frac{2}{8} = \frac{3}{12} = \frac{4}{16} = \frac{5}{20} = \frac{6}{24}$
$= \frac{7}{28} = \frac{8}{32} = \frac{9}{36} = \frac{10}{40} \cdots$
red: $\frac{3}{4} = \frac{6}{8} = \frac{9}{12} = \frac{12}{16} = \frac{15}{20} = \frac{18}{24} = \frac{21}{28}$
$= \frac{24}{32} = \frac{27}{36} = \frac{30}{40} \cdots$

d Answers include any two from each of:

blue: $\frac{1}{4} = \frac{2}{8} = \frac{3}{12} = \frac{4}{16} = \frac{5}{20} = \frac{6}{24}$
$= \frac{7}{28} = \frac{8}{32} = \frac{9}{36} = \frac{10}{40} \cdots$
red: $\frac{3}{4} = \frac{6}{8} = \frac{9}{12} = \frac{12}{16} = \frac{15}{20} = \frac{18}{24} = \frac{21}{28}$
$= \frac{24}{32} = \frac{27}{36} = \frac{30}{40} \cdots$

e Answers include any two from each of:

blue: $\frac{2}{4} = \frac{1}{2} = \frac{4}{8} = \frac{6}{12} = \frac{8}{16} = \frac{10}{20} = \frac{12}{24}$
$= \frac{14}{28} = \frac{16}{32} = \frac{18}{36} = \frac{20}{40} \cdots$
red: $\frac{2}{4} = \frac{1}{2} = \frac{4}{8} = \frac{6}{12} = \frac{8}{16} = \frac{10}{20} = \frac{12}{24}$
$= \frac{14}{28} = \frac{16}{32} = \frac{18}{36} = \frac{20}{40} \cdots$

f Answers include any two from each of:

blue: $\frac{1}{3} = \frac{2}{6} = \frac{3}{9} = \frac{4}{12} = \frac{5}{15} = \frac{6}{18} = \frac{7}{21}$
$= \frac{8}{24} = \frac{9}{27} = \frac{10}{30} \cdots$
red: $\frac{2}{3} = \frac{4}{6} = \frac{6}{9} = \frac{8}{12} = \frac{10}{15} = \frac{12}{18} = \frac{14}{21}$
$= \frac{16}{24} = \frac{18}{27} = \frac{20}{30} \cdots$

3 **a** 10
b 4
c 9
d 4
e 14
f 6
g 9
h 12
i 9

4 **a** $\frac{4}{5}$
b $\frac{3}{4}$
c $\frac{2}{7}$
d $\frac{3}{5}$
e $\frac{3}{4}$
f $\frac{4}{5}$
g $\frac{5}{6}$
h $\frac{1}{8}$

5 $\frac{12}{24} = \frac{21}{42}$
$\frac{14}{28} = \frac{41}{82}$
$\frac{23}{46} = \frac{32}{64}$
$\frac{24}{48} = \frac{42}{84}$
$\frac{34}{68} = \frac{43}{86}$

In each of these fractions the denominator is double the numerator. The units digit in the denominator is double that in the numerator, *and* the tens digit in the denominator is double that in the numerator. The units digits in both the numerator and the denominator must be greater than the tens digits.

PB ■ 16

1 **a** $\frac{2}{8}$ or $\frac{1}{4}$
b $\frac{3}{8}$

c $\frac{3}{8}$

d $\frac{4}{8}$ or $\frac{1}{2}$

e $\frac{5}{8}$

f $\frac{5}{8}$

g $\frac{6}{8}$ or $\frac{3}{4}$

h $\frac{3}{4}$

i $\frac{7}{8}$

2 a $\frac{7}{8}$

b $\frac{6}{8}$ or $\frac{3}{4}$

c $\frac{3}{4}$

d $\frac{5}{8}$

e $\frac{4}{8}$ or $\frac{1}{2}$

f $\frac{2}{4}$ or $\frac{1}{2}$

g $\frac{1}{2}$

h $\frac{3}{8}$

i $\frac{2}{8}$ or $\frac{1}{4}$

3 a $\frac{3}{4}$

b $\frac{7}{8}$

c $\frac{15}{16}$

d $\frac{31}{32}$

e $\frac{63}{64}$

4 a $\frac{7}{3} - \frac{6}{3} + \frac{4}{3} - \frac{2}{3} = \frac{3}{3} = 1$

b Multiple answers are possible, including:

$\frac{1}{3} + \frac{4}{3} + \frac{5}{3} - \frac{7}{3} = \frac{3}{3} = 1$

$\frac{1}{3} + \frac{4}{3} + \frac{6}{3} - \frac{8}{3} = \frac{3}{3} = 1$

$\frac{1}{3} + \frac{4}{3} + \frac{7}{3} - \frac{9}{3} = \frac{3}{3} = 1$

$\frac{1}{3} + \frac{5}{3} + \frac{6}{3} - \frac{9}{3} = \frac{3}{3} = 1$

$\frac{2}{3} + \frac{4}{3} + \frac{5}{3} - \frac{8}{3} = \frac{3}{3} = 1$

$\frac{2}{3} + \frac{4}{3} + \frac{6}{3} - \frac{9}{3} = \frac{3}{3} = 1$

$\frac{5}{3} + \frac{6}{3} - \frac{1}{3} - \frac{7}{3} = \frac{3}{3} = 1$

$\frac{5}{3} + \frac{7}{3} - \frac{1}{3} - \frac{8}{3} = \frac{3}{3} = 1$

$\frac{5}{3} + \frac{8}{3} - \frac{1}{3} - \frac{9}{3} = \frac{3}{3} = 1$

$\frac{5}{3} + \frac{9}{3} - \frac{4}{3} - \frac{7}{3} = \frac{3}{3} = 1$

$\frac{6}{3} + \frac{7}{3} - \frac{8}{3} - \frac{2}{3} = \frac{3}{3} = 1$

$\frac{6}{3} + \frac{7}{3} - \frac{9}{3} - \frac{1}{3} = \frac{3}{3} = 1$

$\frac{6}{3} + \frac{8}{3} - \frac{7}{3} - \frac{4}{3} = \frac{3}{3} = 1$

$\frac{6}{3} + \frac{8}{3} - \frac{9}{3} - \frac{2}{3} = \frac{3}{3} = 1$

$\frac{6}{3} + \frac{9}{3} - \frac{8}{3} - \frac{4}{3} = \frac{3}{3} = 1$

$\frac{6}{3} + \frac{9}{3} - \frac{7}{3} - \frac{5}{3} = \frac{3}{3} = 1$

$\frac{7}{3} + \frac{9}{3} - \frac{8}{3} - \frac{5}{3} = \frac{3}{3} = 1$

$\frac{9}{3} - \frac{4}{3} - \frac{3}{3} + \frac{1}{3} = \frac{3}{3} = 1$

$\frac{9}{3} - \frac{5}{3} - \frac{2}{3} + \frac{1}{3} = \frac{3}{3} = 1$

$\frac{9}{3} - \frac{7}{3} - \frac{1}{3} + \frac{2}{3} = \frac{3}{3} = 1$

$\frac{8}{3} - \frac{4}{3} - \frac{2}{3} + \frac{1}{3} = \frac{3}{3} = 1$

$\frac{7}{3} - \frac{6}{3} - \frac{2}{3} + \frac{4}{3} = \frac{3}{3} = 1$

$\frac{7}{3} - \frac{5}{3} - \frac{1}{3} + \frac{2}{3} = \frac{3}{3} = 1$

Multiple answers are possible.

PB ■ 17

1 a $\frac{1}{8}$

b $\frac{3}{8}$

c $\frac{2}{3}$

2 a $\frac{3}{8}$

b $\frac{1}{3}$

c $\frac{1}{2}$

d $\frac{1}{4}$

3 a $\frac{55}{100}$ or $\frac{11}{20}$

b $\frac{40}{60}$ or $\frac{2}{3}$

c $\frac{24}{1000}$ or $\frac{3}{125}$

d $\frac{1}{3}$

e $\frac{80}{100}$ or $\frac{4}{5}$

f $\frac{33}{60}$ or $\frac{11}{20}$

g $\frac{101}{1000}$

h $\frac{9}{12}$ or $\frac{3}{4}$

4 a $\frac{1}{4}$ turn

b 12:18

c South west

d $\frac{20}{60}$ or $\frac{1}{3}$

e North

PB ■ 18

1 a $(15 \div 3) \times 2 = 10$

b $(21 \div 7) \times 4 = 12$

c $(45 \div 9) \times 7 = 35$
d $(35 \div 5) \times 3 = 21$

2 a 8 m
  b 100 g
  c 8 cm
  d 60 ml
  e 0·9 m or 90 cm
  f 42 g
  g 12 litres
  h 28 cm
  i 60 kg
  j 14 m

3 a £4
  b 16 km
  c 81 kg
  d 1 litre

4 $\frac{1}{5}$ of 30 = 6, $\frac{3}{5}$ of 10 = 6,
$\frac{2}{6}$ of 18 = 6, $\frac{3}{6}$ of 12 = 6,
$\frac{1}{7}$ of 42 = 6, $\frac{3}{7}$ of 14 = 6,
$\frac{3}{8}$ of 16 = 6, $\frac{4}{8}$ of 12 = 6,
$\frac{1}{9}$ of 54 = 6, $\frac{3}{9}$ of 18 = 6

 $\frac{1}{4}$ of 28 = 7,
$\frac{1}{6}$ of 42 = 7, $\frac{3}{6}$ of 14 = 7,
$\frac{1}{7}$ of 49 = 7,
$\frac{1}{8}$ of 56 = 7,
$\frac{1}{9}$ of 63 = 7, $\frac{3}{9}$ of 21 = 7

PB ■ 19

1 a protein: 7·9%
    carbohydrate: 66·8%
    fat: 13·6%
    fibre: 2·1%
    sodium: 0·7%
  b 87·7%
  c 10·5%

2 62·5%

3 a 60
  b 12

a 75
b 27

PB ■ 20

1 a £35·70
  b £59·40
  c £61·47

2

Type of accommodation	Price on 1 January	Price end of June	Price end of December
Flat	£26 000	£28 600	£32 890
Terraced house	£48 000	£50 400	£52 416
Three-bedroomed house	£92 000	£99 360	£94 392
Detached house	£142 000	£150 520	£120 416

3 a £10·80
  b £11·88
  c The pre-sale and post-sale prices
    are different as the shirt was
    reduced by 10% of £12 but at the
    end of the sale the increase was
    10% of the sale price of £10·80
    so it was increased by a smaller
    amount than it was reduced by.

4 a 5760 cm^2
  b 3840 cm^2
  c 9600 cm^2

PB ■ 21

1 a 0·8
  b 1·2
  c 1·6
  d 2·4

2 a 1·25
  b 1·75
  c 2·25
  d 2·75

3 a 12 litres
  b 21 litres

c 27 litres
d 15 litres
e 33 litres
f 9 litres
g 30 litres
h 18 litres

PB ■ 22

1 a Both answers are correct but they
   are shown to a different number
   of decimal places.
  b 0·142 857 142 857
   There is a recurring pattern
   142 857 142 857 …

2 $\frac{1}{2}$ = 0·5
 $\frac{1}{3}$ = 0·333 333 33
 $\frac{1}{4}$ = 0·25
 $\frac{1}{5}$ = 0·2
 $\frac{1}{6}$ = 0·166 666 66
 $\frac{1}{7}$ = 0·142 857 1
 $\frac{1}{8}$ = 0·125
 $\frac{1}{9}$ = 0·111 111 11
 $\frac{1}{10}$ = 0·1
 $\frac{1}{11}$ = 0·090 909
 $\frac{1}{12}$ = 0·083 333 3
 $\frac{1}{13}$ = 0·076 923
 $\frac{1}{14}$ = 0·071 428 5
 $\frac{1}{15}$ = 0·066 666 6
 $\frac{1}{16}$ = 0·0625
 $\frac{1}{17}$ = 0·058 823 5
 $\frac{1}{18}$ = 0·055 555 5
 $\frac{1}{19}$ = 0·052 631 5
 $\frac{1}{20}$ = 0·05

3 a The 3 dots mean that the pattern
   of digits continues.
  b The 2 dots define the sequence
   that recurs.
  c $\frac{2}{7}$ = 0·285 714 285 714…
   $\frac{3}{7}$ = 0·428 571 428 571…
   $\frac{4}{7}$ = 0·571 428 571 428…

$\frac{5}{7}$ = 0·714 285 714 285…
$\frac{6}{7}$ = 0·857 142 857 142…

(?) $\frac{1}{13}$ = 0·076 923 076 923…
 $\frac{2}{13}$ = 0·153 846 153 846…
 $\frac{3}{13}$ = 0·230 769 230 769…
 $\frac{4}{13}$ = 0·307 692 307 692…
 $\frac{5}{13}$ = 0·384 615 384 615…
 $\frac{6}{13}$ = 0·461 538 461 538…
 $\frac{7}{13}$ = 0·538 461 538 461…
 $\frac{8}{13}$ = 0·615 384 615 384…
 $\frac{9}{13}$ = 0·692 307 692 307…
 $\frac{10}{13}$ = 0·769 230 769 230…
 $\frac{11}{13}$ = 0·846 153 846 153…
 $\frac{12}{13}$ = 0·923 076 923 076…

PB ■ 23

1 a red: 2 out of 3, or 2 in 3, or $\frac{2}{3}$, or
   66·7%, or 0·66…
   blue: 1 out of 3, or 1 in 3, or $\frac{1}{3}$, or
   33·3%, or 0·33…
  b red: 1 out of 5, or 1 in 5, or $\frac{1}{5}$, or
   20%, or 0·2
   blue: 4 out of 5, or 4 in 5, or $\frac{4}{5}$, or
   80%, or 0·8
  c red: 3 out of 4, or 3 in 4, or $\frac{3}{4}$, or
   75%, or 0·75
   blue: 1 out of 4, or 1 in 4, or $\frac{1}{4}$, or
   25%, or 0·25

2 Answers are approximate.

	a	b	c
Red	$\frac{1}{3}$	$\frac{9}{20}$	$\frac{1}{4}$
Blue	$\frac{1}{5}$	$\frac{1}{4}$	$\frac{1}{2}$
Yellow	$\frac{1}{7}$	$\frac{1}{10}$	$\frac{1}{20}$
Green	$\frac{1}{5}$	$\frac{1}{10}$	$\frac{1}{7}$
Other	$\frac{1}{7}$	$\frac{1}{10}$	$\frac{1}{20}$

3 a 1 out of 4, or 1 in 4, or $\frac{1}{4}$, or
   25%, or 0·25
  b 3 out of 4, or 3 in 4, or $\frac{3}{4}$, or
   75%, or 0·75

4 a 9 out of 10, or 9 in 10, or $\frac{9}{10}$, or 90%, or 0·9

b 1 out of 10, or 1 in 10, or $\frac{1}{10}$, or 10%, or 0·1

5 red:
Eleanor has 2 out of 5, or 2 in 5, or $\frac{2}{5}$, or 40%, or 0·4
Arash has 3 out of 5, or 3 in 5, or $\frac{3}{5}$, or 60%, or 0·6
blue:
Eleanor has 11 out of 24, or 11 in 24, or $\frac{11}{24}$, or 45·8%, or 0·458
Arash has 13 out of 24, or 13 in 24, or $\frac{13}{24}$, or 54·2%, or 0·542
yellow:
Eleanor has 15 out of 31, or 15 in 31, or $\frac{15}{31}$, or 48·4%, or 0·484
Arash has 16 out of 31, or 16 in 31, or $\frac{16}{31}$, or 51·6%, or 0·516
orange:
Eleanor has 4 out of 9, or 4 in 9, or $\frac{4}{9}$, or 44·4%, or 0·444...
Arash has 5 out of 9, or 5 in 9, or $\frac{5}{9}$, or 55·6%, or 0·555...
green:
Eleanor has 7 out of 16, or 7 in 16, or $\frac{7}{16}$, or 43·75%, or 0·4375
Arash has 9 out of 16, or 9 in 16, or $\frac{9}{16}$, or 56·25%, or 0·5625

PB ■ 24

1 a 1:3
b 2:3
c 1:11
d 2:3
e 1:4
f 3:2
g 2:7
h 4:5
i 10:13
j 7:12

2 a 2:3
b 5:4
c 1:3

3 a Game 1: 36 000:6000 = 6:1
Game 2: 28 000:4000 = 7:1
Game 3: 32 500:2500 = 13:1
Game 4: 30 000:1500 = 20:1
b Game 1

4 Sam gets £50, Ali gets £100

5 90 kg and 150 kg

6 £30

PB ■ 25
1 a–d Child's own word problems.

2 a hat costs £4
scarf costs £2·95
b choc bar costs 45p
can costs 65p
c belt costs £3·80
bag costs £14·40

3 6 people, 4 snakes

4 8 people, 3 dolphins

5 9 frogs, 9 fish

6 a–c Child's own answers based on school day.

PB ■ 26
1 a $8 + 4 \times (2 + 6) + 3$
$= 8 + (4 \times 8) + 3$
$= 8 + 32 + 3$
$= 43$
b $7 - 8 \div 2$
$= 7 - 4$
$= 3$
c $(3 + 2) \times 5$
$= 5 \times 5$
$= 25$
d $6 \times (4 + 3) - 6 \times 2$
$= 6 \times 7 - 6 \times 2$
$= 42 - 12$
$= 30$

e $20 - \dfrac{(6 + 4)}{5}$

$= 20 - 10 \div 5$

$= 20 - 2$

$= 18$

f $\dfrac{(5 + 5 + 7)}{2}$

$= 17 \div 2$

$= 8 \cdot 5$

2 A = 9, B = 8, C = 4

3 a P = 4, Q = 3, R = 7, S = 6

b Child's own codes.

4 Possible answers include the following together with associated reversals in the order of adding and/or multiplying:

$(6 + 4) \times (8 - 3) = 50$

$(3 - 8) \times (6 + 4) = {}^-50$

$(8 - 4) \times (6 + 3) = 36$

$(8 + 4) \times (6 - 3) = 36$

$(4 - 8) \times (6 + 3) = {}^-36$

$(8 + 4) \times (3 - 6) = {}^-36$

$(6 \div 3) \times (8 + 4) = 24$

$(8 + 3) \times (6 - 4) = 22$

$(4 - 6) \times (8 + 3) = {}^-22$

$(8 \div 4) \times (3 + 6) = 18$

$(8 - 6) \times (4 + 3) = 14$

$(8 + 6) \times (4 - 3) = 14$

$(8 + 6) \div (4 - 3) = 14$

$(8 + 6) \div (3 - 4) = {}^-14$

$(8 + 6) \times (3 - 4) = {}^-14$

$(6 - 8) \times (4 + 3) = {}^-14$

$(6 \div 3) \times (8 - 4) = 8$

$(6 \div 3) \times (4 - 8) = {}^-8$

$(8 \div 4) \times (6 - 3) = 6$

$(8 \div 4) \times (3 - 6) = {}^-6$

$(8 + 4) \div (6 - 3) = 4$

$(8 + 4) \div (3 - 6) = {}^-4$

$(6 + 4) \div (8 - 3) = 2$

$(6 + 4) \div (3 - 8) = {}^-2$

(?) $(4 \times 3) - (8 + 3) = 1$

$(6 - 4) \times (4 \div 8) = 1$

$(6 - 4) \times (3 \div 6) = 1$

$(8 - 6) \times (4 \div 8) = 1$

$(8 - 6) \times (3 \div 6) = 1$

$(8 - 6) \times (8 \div 4) = 4$

$(8 - 6) \times (6 \div 3) = 4$

$(6 - 4) \times (8 \div 4) = 4$

$(6 - 4) \times (6 \div 3) = 4$

$(6 \times 3) - (6 + 3) = 9$

$(8 + 4) \times (6 \div 8) = 9$

$(8 + 4) \times (3 \div 4) = 9$

$(6 + 3) \times (4 - 3) = 9$

$(8 - 4) + (4 \times 3) = 16$

$(4 \times 6) + (4 - 3) = 25$

$(8 \times 4) - (4 + 3) = 25$

$(8 \times 3) + (4 - 3) = 25$

$(8 \times 4) + (8 - 4) = 36$

$(8 \times 6) + (4 - 3) = 49$

PB ■ 27

1 a 32 km

b 56 km

c 72 km

d 40 km

e 88 km

f 24 km

g 80 km

h 48 km

2 a 15 miles

b 25 miles

c 35 miles

d 45 miles

e 55 miles

f 20 miles

g 30 miles

h 40 miles

3 a 44 lbs

b 132 lbs

c 330 lbs

d 396 lbs

e 462 lbs

f 550 lbs

g 704 lbs

h 902 lbs

4 Child's own investigation of 2-digit numbers, multiple answers are possible.

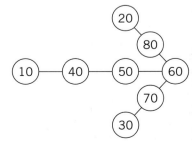? Child's own investigation of 3-digit numbers, multiple answers are possible.

PB ■ 28

1 *a* 2·3
  b 7·4
  c 0·47
  d 1·12
  e 0·39
  f 9·8
  g 9
  h 640 000

2 *a* 28
  b 48
  c 15 800
  d 6600
  e 47
  f 76
  g 670
  h 1580
  i 7800
  j 8700

3 Multiple answers are possible.

? Multiple answers are possible.

PB ■ 29

1 *a* 21
  b 110
  c **24** + 63 = 87
  d **99** − 57 = 42
  e 15
  f 107
  g 51 + **38** = 89
  h 87 − **45** = 42

2 *a* 27 + 18 = 45 and 74 − 29 = 45
  b 39 + 19 = 58 and 84 − 26 = 58
  c 26 + 37 = 63 and 81 − 18 = 63
  d 16 + 53 = 69, 96 − 27 = 69 and 85 − 16 = 69
  e 15 + 67 = 82, 33 + 49 = 82 and 97 − 15 = 82
  f 24 + 29 = 53 and 98 − 45 = 53

3 Child's own investigation to show that: the most common totals are 132, 133 and 134 because it results from 3 different combinations of dice numbers rolled; the least common totals are 128, 129, 137 and 138 because they each result from just one combination of dice numbers rolled. The mean average of the totals is expected to be 133.

PB ■ 30

1 A = 2, B = 9

2 Routes for target numbers between 5 and 20:
  20 + 8 + 7 − 6 − 13 − 11 = 5
  20 + 8 − 9 − 7 + 13 − 11 = 14
  20 + 8 − 9 − 7 − 8 + 11 = 15
  20 − 6 + 9 + 6 − 13 − 11 = 5
  20 − 6 + 9 − 7 + 13 − 11 = 18
  20 − 6 − 4 + 7 + 13 − 11 = 19

3 *a–b*

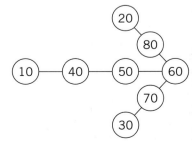

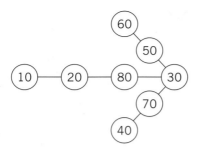

4 Multiple answers are possible, making all the odd numbers from 1 to 29.

Multiple answers are possible.

PB ■ 31

1 a 84 442
b 79 304
c 159 968

2 a 88 412
b £659 901
c £473 907
d 94 921
e £79 492
f £3 136 320

PB ■ 32

1 a 133·87
b 146·04
c 139·82
d 170·8
e 139·41
Triangle **a** has the smallest total.

2 a 73·85
b 21·83
c 2·89
d 8·32

3 11·1 + 1·11 = 12·21
22·2 + 2·22 = 24·42

33·3 + 3·33 = 36·63
44·4 + 4·44 = 48·84
55·5 + 5·55 = 61·05
66·6 + 6·66 = 73·26
77·7 + 7·77 = 85·47
88·8 + 8·88 = 97·68
99·9 + 9·99 = 109·89
The hundredths digit increases by 1 each time.
The tenths digit increases by 2 each time.
The difference between each pair of consecutive answers is 12·21.

The pattern in the answers is
112·211
224·422
336·633
and the difference between consecutive answers is 112·211.

PB ■ 33

1 a 12 345
b 34 567
c 56 789
The answers are the reverse of the original number subtracted from.

2 530 865

3 6 419 754

4 75 308 643

5 a The 5-digit numbers are made using the digits in reverse order each time, starting again from 9 when 0 is reached.
b 98 765 − 43 210 = 55 555
87 654 − 32 109 = 55 545
76 543 − 21 098 = 55 445
65 432 − 10 987 = 54 445
54 321 − 09 876 = 44 445
c 55 555 − 55 545 = 10
55 545 − 55 445 = 100

$55\,445 - 54\,445 = 1000$
$54\,445 - 44\,445 = 10\,000$

d The difference between consecutive answers increases by a factor of 10 each time.

PB ■ 34

1 a

9·39	**11·26**	6·11
5·64	**8·92**	**12·2**
11·73	**6·58**	8·45

b

7·61	9·48	4·33
3·86	7·14	10·42
9·95	4·8	6·67

Total for each row, column or diagonal = 21·42

2 $9·6 - 8·75 = 0·85$
$9·5 - 8·76 = 0·74$
$9·5 - 8·67 = 0·83$
$8·6 - 7·95 = 0·65$
$8·5 - 7·96 = 0·54$
$8·5 - 7·69 = 0·81$
$7·8 - 6·95 = 0·85$
$7·5 - 6·98 = 0·52$
$7·5 - 6·89 = 0·61$
$6·8 - 5·97 = 0·83$
$6·7 - 5·98 = 0·72$
$6·7 - 5·89 = 0·81$

3 $11·1 - 1·11 = 9·99$
$22·2 - 2·22 = 19·98$
$33·3 - 3·33 = 29·97$
$44·4 - 4·44 = 39·96$
$55·5 - 5·55 = 49·95$
$66·6 - 6·66 = 59·94$
$77·7 - 7·77 = 69·93$
$88·8 - 8·88 = 79·92$
$99·9 - 9·99 = 89·91$
The hundredths digit decreases by 1 each time.
The tenths digit is 9 each time.
? The difference between each pair of consecutive answers is 9·99.
Each answer is a multiple of 9·99.

PB ■ 35

1 a $1·68 + 5·5 = 7·18$
b $3·31 - 1·17 = 2·14$
c $6·5 + 12·0 = 18·5$, or
$6·5 + 1·20 = 7·7$
d $2·7 + 6·31 = 9·01$
e $24·6 - 5·6 = 19$
f $20·9 - 11·0 = 9·9$, or
$20·9 - 1·10 = 19·8$, or
$2·09 - 1·10 = 0·99$

2 a

	0·2	
0·6	0·1	0·4
	0·3	
	0·5	

b

	0·1	
0·5	0·3	0·4
	0·2	
	0·6	

3 0·7 on the back of 0·5
0·3 on the back of 0·6
0·2 on the back of 0·8

4 Multiple answers are possible.

? Multiple answers are possible.

PB ■ 36

1 a 4704
b 7595
c 12 136
d 19 826
e 33 705
f 29 986

2 a 5610 m²
b 9108 m²
c 12 894 m²
d 23 618 m²
e 26 659 m²

3 120 different answers are possible.
$762 \times 84 = 64\,008$ gives the largest answer.

$478 \times 26 = 12\,428$ gives the smallest answer.

? 120 different answers are possible.
$7642 \times 8 = 61\,136$ gives the largest product.
$4678 \times 2 = 9356$ gives the smallest product.

PB ■ 37

1 a $9 \times 9 + 7 = 88$
$98 \times 9 + 6 = 888$
$987 \times 9 + 5 = 8888$
$9876 \times 9 + 4 = 88888$
$98765 \times 9 + 3 = 888\,888$

b The answer digits are always 8. The difference between consecutive answers increases by a factor of ten each time.

c $987\,654 \times 9 + 2 = 8\,888\,888$
$9\,876\,543 \times 9 + 1 = 88\,888\,888$

2 a $1 \cdot 2 \times 9 + 0 \cdot 3 = 11 \cdot 1$
$12 \cdot 3 \times 9 + 0 \cdot 4 = 111 \cdot 1$
$123 \cdot 4 \times 9 + 0 \cdot 5 = 1111 \cdot 1$
$1234 \cdot 5 \times 9 + 0 \cdot 6 = 11\,111 \cdot 1$
$12345 \cdot 6 \times 9 + 0 \cdot 7 = 111\,111 \cdot 1$

b The answer digits are always 1. The difference between consecutive answers increases by a factor of ten each time.

c $123\,456 \cdot 7 \times 9 + 0 \cdot 8$
$= 1\,111\,111 \cdot 1$

3 120 different answers are possible.
$743 \cdot 2 \times 8 = 5945 \cdot 6$ gives the largest product.
$347 \cdot 8 \times 2 = 695 \cdot 6$ gives the smallest product.

? 120 different answers are possible.
$74 \cdot 2 \times 83 = 6158 \cdot 6$ gives the largest answer.

$37 \cdot 8 \times 24 = 907 \cdot 2$ gives the smallest answer.

PB ■ 38

1 a $158 \cdot 73 \times 2 \times 7 = 2222 \cdot 22$
$158 \cdot 73 \times 3 \times 7 = 3333 \cdot 33$
$158 \cdot 73 \times 5 \times 7 = 5555 \cdot 55$
$158 \cdot 73 \times 9 \times 7 = 9999 \cdot 99$

b The answers are recurring sets of the digit that has been multiplied by 7 and $158 \cdot 73$

c $158 \cdot 73 \times 4 \times 7 = 4444 \cdot 44$
$158 \cdot 73 \times 6 \times 7 = 6666 \cdot 66$
$158 \cdot 73 \times 7 \times 7 = 7777 \cdot 77$

2 a $22\,222 \cdot 2$
b $555 \cdot 555$
c $2222 \cdot 22$
d $33 \cdot 3333$
e $6666 \cdot 66$
f $999 \cdot 999$
g $77 \cdot 7777$
h $4 \cdot 444\,44$

3 $1 \cdot 43 \times 1 \times 7 = 10 \cdot 01$
$1 \cdot 43 \times 2 \times 7 = 20 \cdot 02$
$1 \cdot 43 \times 3 \times 7 = 30 \cdot 03$
$1 \cdot 43 \times 4 \times 7 = 40 \cdot 04$
$1 \cdot 43 \times 5 \times 7 = 50 \cdot 05$
$1 \cdot 43 \times 6 \times 7 = 60 \cdot 06$
$1 \cdot 43 \times 7 \times 7 = 70 \cdot 07$
$1 \cdot 43 \times 8 \times 7 = 80 \cdot 08$
$1 \cdot 43 \times 9 \times 7 = 90 \cdot 09$
The answers are all multiples of $10 \cdot 01$.

? $14 \cdot 3 \times 1 \times 7 = 100 \cdot 1$
$14 \cdot 3 \times 2 \times 7 = 200 \cdot 2$
$14 \cdot 3 \times 3 \times 7 = 300 \cdot 3$
$14 \cdot 3 \times 4 \times 7 = 400 \cdot 4$
$14 \cdot 3 \times 5 \times 7 = 500 \cdot 5$
$14 \cdot 3 \times 6 \times 7 = 600 \cdot 6$
$14 \cdot 3 \times 7 \times 7 = 700 \cdot 7$
$14 \cdot 3 \times 8 \times 7 = 800 \cdot 8$
$14 \cdot 3 \times 9 \times 7 = 900 \cdot 9$
The answers are all multiples of $100 \cdot 1$.

PB ■ 39

1 a 95 r 1, $95\frac{1}{4}$ or 95·25
  b 114
  c 96 r 2, $96\frac{2}{5}$ or 96·4
  d 106 r 1, $106\frac{1}{5}$ or 106·2
  e 134 r 4, $134\frac{4}{5}$ or 134·8
  f 78 r 5, $78\frac{5}{8}$ or 78·625
  g 101 r 7, $101\frac{7}{8}$ or 101·875
  h 123 r 3, $123\frac{3}{8}$ or 123·375

2 a 39p
  b £1·42
  c 72
  d 154 km
  e 184·8 km

PB ■ 40

1 a 406 ÷ 7 = **58**
  b 539 ÷ 7 = **77**
  c 963 ÷ 9 = **107**
  d 528 ÷ **88** = 6
  e 592 ÷ **74** = 8
  f 956 ÷ **239** = 4

2 a 390 ÷ 13 = **30**
  b 665 ÷ 19 = **35**
  c 962 ÷ 37 = **26**
  d 828 ÷ **18** = 46
  e 901 ÷ **17** = 53
  f 948 ÷ **12** = 79

3

calories	food item	quantity
360	eggs	5
372	slices of bread	6
588	sausages	7
752	cereal portions	8
594	cheese portions	6
261	potato portions	3

PB ■ 41

1 a 65 ÷ 2 = 32·5
    65 ÷ 3 = 21·6666667
    65 ÷ 4 = 16·25
    65 ÷ 5 = 13
    65 ÷ 6 = 10·833 333 3
  b 73 ÷ 2 = 36·5
    73 ÷ 3 = 24·333 333 3
    73 ÷ 4 = 18·25
    73 ÷ 5 = 14·6
    73 ÷ 6 = 12·166 666 7
  c 83 ÷ 2 = 41·5
    83 ÷ 3 = 27·666 666 7
    83 ÷ 4 = 20·75
    83 ÷ 5 = 16·6
    83 ÷ 6 = 13·833 333 3

2 a £1·63, £1·35, £1·44
  b 1 box of 40 @ £57·60:
    £1·44 per CD; or 1 box of 15 @
    £24·45 + 1 box of 25 @ £33·75:
    £58·20 for 40, £1·46 per CD
    (rounded to the nearest penny)
  c 1 box of 25 @ £33·75 + 1 box of
    40 @ £57·60: £91·35 for 65,
    £1·41 per CD; or 2 boxes of 25 @
    £33·75 + 1 box of 15 @ £24·45:
    £91·95 for 65, £1·41 per CD
  d 2 boxes of 40 @ £57·60:
    £115·20 for 80, £1·44 per CD;
    or 2 boxes of 15 @ £24·45 + 2
    boxes of 25 @ £33·75: £116·40
    for 80, £1·46 per CD; or 1 box of
    25 @ £33·75 + 1 box of 15 @
    £24·45 + 1 box of 40 @
    £57·60: £115·80 for 80, £1·45
    per CD

PB ■ 42

1 a 9·5 kg sugar
    13·5 kg flour
    1·25 kg salt
    15·7 kg apples
    14·3 litres milk
  b 5·8 kg tea
    10·9 kg flour
    18·35 kg potatoes
    21·15 kg meat
    31·3 litres milk

2 a 202·8

b

13·76	10·62	26·32
29·46	16·9	4·34
7·48	23·18	20·04

Total for each row, column or diagonal = 50·7
This is a magic square because each number is one quarter the size of the corresponding number in the first grid. Therefore the total of each row, column and diagonal must be one quarter of that in the original magic square.

3 Multiple answers are possible.
largest possible answer:
$874·3 ÷ 2 = 437·15$
smallest possible answer:
$234·7 ÷ 8 = 29·34$

? Multiple answers are possible.
largest possible answer:
$87·43 ÷ 2 = 43·715$
smallest possible answer:
$23·47 ÷ 8 = 2·934$

PB ■ 43

1 a 29 cm
  b 19
  c 52 miles
  d 11

2 a A = 1
    B = 6
    C = 2
    D = 9
  b A = 2
    B = 5
    C = 3
    D = 1
  c A = 2
    B = 1

C = 7
D = 3

PB ■ 44

1 a $99 + (9 ÷ 9) = 100$
  b $44 + 44 + (4 × 4) − 4 = 100$
  c $(5 × 5 × 5) − (5 × 5) = 100$
  d $(33 × 3) + (3 ÷ 3) = 100$
  e $666 ÷ 6 − (6 + 6) + (6 ÷ 6)$
    $= 100$

2 a $(3 + 6) × (23 − 11) = 9 × 12$
    $= 108$
  b $(38 + 29) × (35 − 12) = 67 × 23$
    $= 1541$
  c $(29 + 47) × (58 − 28) = 76 × 30$
    $= 2280$

3 $(473 + 378) × (289 + 137)$
    $= 851 × 426 = 362\,526$
    $(473 + 289) × (378 + 137)$
    $= 762 × 515 = 392\,430$
    $(473 + 137) × (378 + 289)$
    $= 610 × 667 = 406\,870$
Reversals of the order of adding and/or multiplying are possible.
smallest possible answer: 362 526
largest possible answer: 406 870

? Smallest possible positive answer:
$(473 − 378) × (289 − 137) = 14\,440$
Smallest possible answer:
$(473 − 289) ×(137 − 378)$
$= ^-44\,344$
or
$(289 − 473) × (378 − 137)$
$= ^-44\,344$
Largest possible answer:
$(473 − 289) × (378 − 137)$
$= 44\,344$

PB ■ 45

1 a 1288
  b 3483

c 36 270
d 63
e 547
f 369

2 $256 \times 497 = 127\,232$
$256 \times 718 = 183\,808$
$256 \times 603 = 154\,368$
$497 \times 718 = 356\,846$
$497 \times 603 = 299\,691$
$718 \times 603 = 432\,954$

3 a The units digit of the total cost is a 1 so the units digit of his change should be a 9.
b Because 26p is close to 25p which means roughly 4 stamps for every £1. Mel had £5 so she can buy around 20 stamps.
c Sunil has spent more than £10. Just looking at the pounds, he has spent £5 + £2 + £2 + £1 = £10 so his change cannot be more than £10.
d Ali forgot to convert the 49p into £0·49

(?) even – because subtracting one from the product of an odd number and an even number gives an odd number.

PB ■ 46
1 a $(810 \div 135) \times 9 = 54$
b $16\,875 = 25 \times (810 - 135)$ or $16\,875 \div 25 = 810 - 135$
c $810 \times 135 - 50\,300 = 59\,050$
d $810 + 135 = 954 - 9$

2 a P = 2
Q = 5
R = 3
S = 1

b P = 1
Q = 6
R = 2
S = 9

3 a 37, 38, 39
b 21, 23, 25
c 16, 25, 36
d 17, 19, 23

4 a $123 + 45 - 67 + 8 - 9 = 100$
b Possible ways of making 100 include:
$1 + 2 + 34 - 5 + 67 - 8 + 9 = 100$
$12 + 3 - 4 + 5 + 67 + 8 + 9 = 100$
$123 - 4 - 5 - 6 - 7 + 8 - 9 = 100$
$123 + 4 - 5 + 67 - 89 = 100$
$123 - 45 - 67 + 89 = 100$

(?) $9 + 8 + 76 + 5 - 4 + 3 + 2 + 1 = 100$ is one way of making 100.
$9 \times 8 + 7 \times 6 - 5 - 4 - 3 - 2 \times 1 = 100$ is another.

5 $517 \times 39 = 20\,163$
$3791 \times 5 = 18\,955$
Multiple answers are possible.
$951 \times 73 = 69\,423$ is the greatest answer.
$159 \times 37 = 5883$ is the lowest answer.

(?) Multiple answers are possible.
$840 \times 62 = 52\,080$ is the greatest answer.
$048 \times 26 = 1248$ is the lowest answer.

PB ■ 47
1 a £2850 of tickets given away
b 111 tickets unused
c 978 children paid for a ticket

d 1467 children at the fair
e 7445 women at the fair
f £164 085 collected for adult tickets
g £168 730·50 collected for all paid tickets
h £178 274·22 total money spent
i £14·37 spent per person

2 a Jeremy has more euros
b 12·25 euros more

PB ■ 48

1 41 photos

2 £11 220

3 £35·20

4 a £6264
b 36 months (or 3 years)

5 £471

6 3·75 Australian dollars

7 7p per nut

PB ■ 49

1 a $n + 3$
b $7 + n$
c $10 - n$
d $n - 4$
e $3n + 2$
f $\dfrac{n}{4}$
g $5n - 8$
h $\dfrac{9}{n}$
i n^2
j $2(n - 4)$

2 a a number add 10
b a number multiplied by 4 and 1 subtracted

c multiply a number by 2 and add 3
d a number multiplied by 6
e a number divided by 3
f 5 minus a number
g a number multiplied by 3 and 2 subtracted
h a number minus 2 then multiplied by 3
i a number multiplied by 3 and 6 subtracted

3 Top row:
$x - z + x + y + z + x - y$
$= x + x + x - z + z + y - y$
$= 3x$
Middle row:
$x - y + z + x + x + y - z$
$= x + x + x - y + y + z - z$
$= 3x$
Bottom row:
$x + y + x - y - z + x + z$
$= x + x + x + y - y - z + z$
$= 3x$
1st column:
$x - z + x - y + z + x + y$
$= x + x + x - z + z - y + y$
$= 3x$
2nd column:
$x + y + z + x + x - y - z$
$= x + x + x + y - y + z - z$
$= 3x$
3rd column:
$x - y + x + y - z + x + z$
$= x + x + x - y + y - z + z$
$= 3x$
Diagonal top left to bottom right:
$x - z + x + x + z$
$= x + x + x - z + z$
$= 3x$
Diagonal bottom left to top right:
$x + y + x + x - y$
$= x + x + x + y - y$
$= 3x$
Child's own magic squares completed by working out the expressions given for values of x, y

and z of own choice· The magic number of each square will be the value selected for x multiplied by 3.

? For a square with magic number 12, x will always be 4 (12 ÷ 3) but y and z can have any value. Child's own magic squares with magic number of 12.

PB ■ 50

1 a

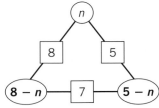

$8 - n + 5 - n = 7$
$8 + 5 - n - n = 7$
$13 - 2n = 7$
$2n = 6$
$n = 3$

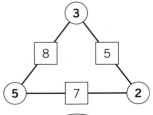

b

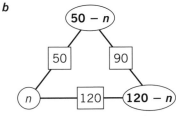

$50 - n + 120 - n = 90$
$50 + 120 - n - n = 90$
$170 - 2n = 90$
$2n = 80$
$n = 40$

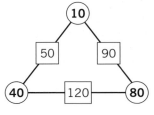

c

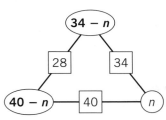

$34 - n + 40 - n = 28$
$34 + 40 - n - n = 28$
$74 - 2n = 28$
$2n = 46$
$n = 23$

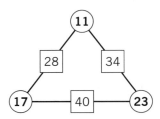

2 a If negative numbers are used, there is an infinite number of solutions for this arithmagon.

b The sum of the corner numbers is half that of the numbers in the squares.

?

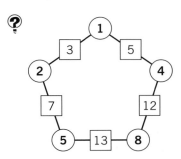

PB ■ 51

1 **a** $m = 60h$

m = minutes, h = hours or child's own letters to represent minutes and hours

b $y = \dfrac{m}{12}$

y = age in years, m = age in months or child's own letters to represent age in years and months

c $A = \dfrac{b \times h}{2}$ or $A = \dfrac{bh}{2}$

A = area of triangle, b = base, h = height or child's own letters to represent area, base and height

d $d = st$

d = distance, s = speed, t = time or child's own letters to represent distance, speed and time

2 **a** Area of a rectangle = length $\times$ width

A = lw		
l	*w*	*A*
3	7	21
9	5	45
8	12	96
6	12	72
5	11	55

b metres = centimetres $\div$ 100

m = c ÷ 100	
m	*c*
2	200
4·5	450
7·25	725
10·5	1050
10·85	1085

c Perimeter of a rectangle = double the length plus double the width

P = 2l + 2w		
l	*w*	*P*
8	4	24
12	6	36
7	5	24
5	8	26
6	9	30

3 **a** $n + 7 = 12$
$n = 5$

b $n - 15 = 15$
$n = 30$

c $3n = 12$
$n = 4$

d $\dfrac{n}{7} = 4$
$n = 28$

e $5n + 2 = 12$
$n = 2$

PB ■ 52

1 **a**

Shape number (*n*)	Number of squares (*s*)
1	5
2	7
3	9
4	11
5	13
6	15
7	17
8	19

b $s = 2n + 3$

26

2 a

Number of rectangles (R)	Number of triangles (T)
2	2
3	4
4	6
5	8
6	10
7	12
8	14
9	16

b $T = 2R - 2$

3 Multiple answers are possible following the relationship,
▲ − ■ = 1:

■	▲
1	2
2	3
3	4
4	5
5	6
6	7
7	8
8	9
9	10

? Multiple answers are possible following the relationship,
▲ − ■ = 4:

■	▲
1	5
2	6
3	7
4	8
5	9
6	10
7	11
8	12
9	13

PB ■ 53

1 a 1, 1, 2, 3, 5, 8, 13, 21, 34, 55, 89, 144, 233, 377, 610

b 3, 6, 9, 15, 24, 39, 63, 102, 165, 267, 432, 699, 1131, 1830, 2961

c 4, ⁻1, 3, 2, 5, 7, 12, 19, 31, 50, 81,131, 212, 343, 555

d ⁻2, 0, ⁻2, ⁻2, ⁻4, ⁻6, ⁻10, ⁻16, ⁻26, ⁻42, ⁻68, ⁻110, ⁻178, ⁻288, ⁻466

2 a

b The decimal number sequence shows the quotient of consecutive terms is tending to 0·618.

3 a $F(1) + F(2) + F(3) + ... = 143$
$11 \times F(7) = 143$

PUPIL BOOK

b The two answers are the same.

c The relationship holds true for other Fibonacci sequences.

PB ■ 54

1 a 7, 11, 15, 19, 23, 27, 31, 35

b $\frac{1}{9}$, $\frac{1}{3}$, 1, 3, 9, 27, 81, 243

2 a Child's constructed shapes.

b

Shape	Value (number of cubes)
L(1)	3
L(2)	5
L(3)	7
L(4)	9
L(5)	11
L(6)	13
L(7)	15

c $L(n) = 2n + 1 \therefore L(10) = 21$, $L(20) = 41$

3 a

Shape	Value (number of cubes)
T(1)	4
T(2)	7
T(3)	10
T(4)	13
T(5)	16
T(6)	19

$T(n) = 3n + 1 \therefore T(25) = 76$

b

Shape	Value (number of cubes)
X(1)	5
X(2)	9
X(3)	13
X(4)	17
X(5)	21
X(6)	25

$X(n) = 4n + 1 \therefore X(52) = 209$

c

Shape	Value (number of cubes)
C(1)	5
C(2)	8
C(3)	11
C(4)	14
C(5)	17
C(6)	20

$C(n) = 3n + 2 \therefore C(100) = 302$

4 Kelly's and Greg's sequences are both correct. Other possible rules include:
$\times 2 + 2$:
3, 8, 18, 38, 78, 158 …
$\times 4 - 4$:
3, 8, 28, 108, 428, 1708 …

PB ■ 55

1 a $n \rightarrow n + 2$

b $n \rightarrow 3n$

c $n \rightarrow 2(n - 1)$

d $n \rightarrow 2n + 6$

e $n \rightarrow n^2$

2 a nth term $= 3n$

b nth term $= 2n + 6$

c nth term $= n^2$

d nth term $= 3n + 1$

(?) Child's own sequence and rule for
*n*th term.

PB ■ 56

1 a rule: $x + 2 = y$
  b rule: $x + 7 = y$
  c rule: $x - 6 = y$
  d rule: $x - 10 = y$

2 a $x + 6 = y$
  b $x + 4 = y$
  c $x + 3 = y$
  d $x - 2 = y$
  e $x - 4 = y$
  f $x - 8 = y$

3

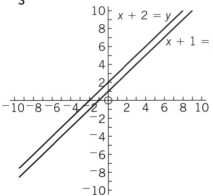

$x + 1 = y$ crosses the *y*-axis at (0, 1)
$x + 2 = y$ crosses the *y*-axis at (0, 2)
$x + 4 = y$ crosses the *y*-axis at (0, 4)
$x - 7 = y$ crosses the *y*-axis at (0, ⁻7)
$x + 6 = y$ crosses the *y*-axis at (0, 6)
$x - 2 = y$ crosses the *y*-axis at (0, ⁻2)
A line $x + n = y$ will cross the *y*-axis
at (0, *n*)
A line $x - n = y$ will cross the *y*-axis
at (0, ⁻*n*)

PB ■ 57

1 a $5x = y$
  b $9x = y$
  c $7x = y$

2 a $5x = y$
  b $3x = y$
  c $2x = y$
  d $x = y$
  e $\frac{1}{2}x = y$

3

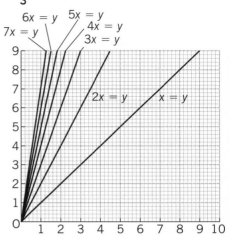

Angle between line $x = y$ and
x-axis = 45°
Angle between line $2x = y$ and
x-axis = 64°
Angle between line $3x = y$ and
x-axis = 72°
Angle between line $4x = y$ and
x-axis = 76°
Angle between line $5x = y$ and
x-axis = 79°
Angle between line $6x = y$ and
x-axis = 81°
Angle between line $7x = y$ and
x-axis = 82°
As the value of *n* in the equation
$y = nx$ increases, so the lines get
steeper and the angle they make
with the x-axis increases. However,
the difference between successive
angles decreases as the lines get
steeper.

1

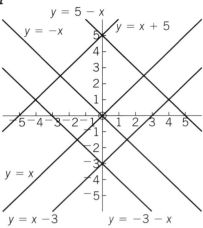

$y = 5 - x$

$y = -x$

$y = x + 5$

$y = x$

$y = x - 3$ $y = -3 - x$

a The graphs all have the same positive slope.

b The graphs all have the form $y = x \pm n$, the relationship of x:y is the same for each equation.

c Line $y = x$ crosses the x-axis at (0, 0) and the y-axis at (0, 0)
Line $y = x - 3$ crosses the x-axis at (3, 0) and the y-axis at (0, ⁻3)
Line $y = x + 5$ crosses the x-axis at (⁻5, 0) and the y-axis at (0, 5)

2 a The graphs all have the same negative slope.

b The graphs all have the form $y = -x \pm n$, the basic relationship of $1x$:$1y$ is the same for each equation.

c Line $y = -x$ crosses the x-axis at (0, 0) and the y-axis at (0, 0)
Line $y = 5 - x$ crosses the x-axis at (5, 0) and the y-axis at (0, 5)
Line $y = -3 - x$ crosses the x-axis at (⁻3, 0) and the y-axis at (0, ⁻3)

3 a

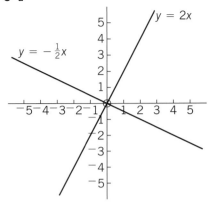

$y = 2x$

$y = -\frac{1}{2}x$

b The two lines cross at 90° to each other.

c Multiple answers are possible, including any one of: $y = x$, $y = x + 5$, or $y = x - 3$ with any one of: $y = -x$, $y = 5 - x$, or $y = -3 - x$

1 OP = 8 mm = 0·8 cm = 0·008 m
PQ = 11 mm = 1·1 cm = 0·011 m
QR = 28 mm = 2·8 cm = 0·028 m
RS = 27 mm = 2·7 cm = 0·027 m
ST = 17 mm = 1·7 cm = 0·017 m

2 a 775 mm
b 420 mm
c 230 mm
d 2440 mm
e 1530 mm
f 625 mm

3 a 560 m
b 14·56 km

4 a 525 m
b 10·9 days
c 105 m

PB ■ 60

1 27 m

2 *a* 64 pieces
   b 0·5 m

3 *a* 116 m
   b 174 m
   c 290 m

4 0·1 mm to 1 decimal place

PB ■ 61

1 A + 1 = 475 mm + 25 inches
   (page example)
   A + 2 = 475 mm + 10 inches
     ≈47·5 cm + (10 × 2·5) cm
     ≈72·5 cm
   A + 3 = 475 mm + 1 foot
     ≈47·5 cm + 30 cm
     ≈77·5 cm
   B + 1 = 60 cm + 25 inches
     ≈60 cm + (25 × 2·5) cm
     ≈122·5 cm
   B + 2 = 60 cm + 10 inches
     ≈60 cm + (10 × 2·5) cm
     ≈85 cm
   B + 3 = 60 cm + 1 foot
     ≈60 cm + 30 cm
     ≈90 cm
   C + 1 = 0·125 m + 25 inches
     ≈12·5 cm + (25 × 2·5) cm
     ≈75 cm
   C + 2 = 0·125 mm + 10 inches
     ≈12·5 cm + (10 × 2·5) cm
     ≈37·5 cm
   C + 3 = 0·125 mm + 1 foot
     ≈12·5 cm + (1 × 30) cm
     ≈42·5 cm

2 Dundee: 34 km
   Edinburgh: 66 km
   Glasgow: 91 km
   London: 666 km
   Stirling: 53 km
   Oxford: 624 km

3 Cardiff: 106 miles
   London: 57 miles
   Manchester: 144 miles
   Newcastle: 260 miles
   Nottingham: 98 miles
   Perth: 390 miles

PB ■ 62

1 *a* £40
   b £80
   c £30
   d £100

2 *a* 120 g
   b 190 g
   c 160 g
   d 250 g
   e 325 g
   f 325 g
   g 356 g
   h 356 g

3 *a* 4 oz
   b 6 oz
   c 5 oz
   d 8 oz
   e 11 oz
   f 11 oz
   g 12 oz
   h 12 oz

4 *a* 8·9 kg
   b 19·6 lbs

5 *a* £45
   b £40
   c £100

PB ■ 63

1 *a* 34·8 kg
   b 6·4 tonnes
   c 1·044 tonnes

2 a 1760
  b 2640 g

3 a Sausages
  b Cod
  c Beefburger

4 a 30 servings
  b chips: 510 g fat
    roast potatoes: 240 g fat
    baked potatoes: 3 g fat

5 a 1·95 g
  b 39 g

PB ■ 64

1 a

Number of gallons	Number of litres
2	9
4	18
6	27
8	36
10	45
12	54

b

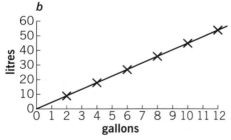

Points are plotted as follows:
(2, 9)
(4, 18)
(6, 27)
(8, 36)
(10, 45)
(12, 54).

2 a 14 litres
  b 23 litres
  c 41 litres
  d 50 litres
  e 13 litres
  f 38 litres
  g 43 litres
  h 46 litres

3 a 2·2 gallons
  b 5·6 gallons
  c 10·0 gallons
  d 11·1 gallons
  e 7·6 gallons
  f 10·4 gallons
  g 2·7 gallons
  h 8·2 gallons

4 a 160 pints
  b 90 litres

? 12 gallons

PB ■ 65

1 Multiple answers are possible, including:

X		X		
		X		X
X				X
	X		X	
	X		X	

X	X		
		X	X
X	X		
		X	X
X		X	

	X		X	
	X		X	
X				X
X		X		
		X		X

X		X		
	X			X
	X		X	
X				X
		X	X	

	X		X	
		X		X
X				X
	X	X		
X			X	

	X	X		
X				X
	X		X	
X			X	
		X		X

	X			X
		X	X	
X				X
X		X		
	X		X	

2 12 ml + 30 ml + 38 ml in one container
8 ml + 24 ml + 48 ml in the other

3 Child's own working to show the answer either 1·089 or 0.

(?) The most common answer is 10·89, but multiple answers are possible.

PB ■ 66

1 a Answer depends on the current year:
2003: 2779
2004: 2780
2005: 2781
2006: 2782
2007: 2783
2008: 2784
2009: 2785
2010: 2786
b 384 years
c 97
d 2288 years
e Answer depends on the current year:
2003 to July 2004: 24
September 2004 to July 2008: 25
After July 2008: 26
f Answer depends on the current year:
2003 to July 2004: 121
September 2004 to July 2008: 122
After July 2008: 123
g 2032

2 a 63
b 72
c 75
d 116
e 84

3 a–b Multiple answers are possible.

4 The date exactly half way through the year is 2nd July. In a leap year the half way point falls at midnight at the end of 2nd July.

PB ■ 67

1 a 13:00
b 20:00
c 15:00

d 09:00
e 05:00
f 14:00
g 20:00
h 07:00
i 19:00
j 08:00

2 a San Francisco: 06:00
Nairobi: 17:00
Sydney: Midnight, 00:00
b 14:00

3 a 09:30
b 17:30
c 18:30
d 21:30
e 19:30
f 11:30

4 a Oslo: 18:00
San Francisco: 09:00
b two of: Beijing, Perth, Hong Kong

5 a 10:15 23rd May
b 03:15 23rd May

PB ■ 68

1 a Any 2 from:
$(10 \times 6) + (6 \times 4) = 60 + 24$
$= 84 \, cm^2$,
$(6 \times 6) + (12 \times 4) = 36 + 48$
$= 84 \, cm^2$,
$(12 \times 10) - (6 \times 6)$
$= 120 - 36 = 84 \, cm^2$
b Any 2 from:
$(20 \times 11) + (20 \times 5)$
$= 220 + 100 = 320 \, cm^2$,
$(9 \times 5) + (16 \times 11) + (11 \times 9)$
$= 45 + 176 + 99 = 320 \, cm^2$,
$(29 \times 16) - (11 \times 9) - (9 \times 5)$
$= 464 - 99 - 45 = 320 \, cm^2$

c Any 2 from:
$(15 \times 5) + (5 \times 5) + (15 \times 5)$
$= 75 + 25 + 75 = 175 \, cm^2$,
$(15 \times 5) + (10 \times 5) + (10 \times 5)$
$= 75 + 50 + 50 = 175 \, cm^2$,
$(15 \times 15) - (10 \times 5)$
$= 225 - 50 = 175 \, cm^2$

2 a $A = l \times b = 6 \times 6 = 36 \, cm^2$
$P = 2(l + b) = 2(6 + 6) = 24 \, cm$
b $A = l \times b = 7 \times 3 \cdot 5 = 24 \cdot 5 \, cm^2$
$P = 2(l + b) = 2(7 + 3 \cdot 5) = 21 \, cm$
c $A = l \times b = 18 \times 18 = 324 \, cm^2$
$P = 2(l + b) = 2(18 + 18) = 72 \, cm$

3 a $l = 12 \, cm$, $b = 4 \, cm$
b $l = 10 \, cm$, $b = 7 \, cm$
c $l = 15 \, cm$, $b = 6 \, cm$
d $l = 24 \, cm$, $b = 4 \, cm$
e $l = 12 \, cm$, $b = 12 \, cm$

PB ■ 69

1 a 4·5 square units
b 6 square units
c 8 square units
d 12 square units

2 a $A = \frac{1}{2}(4 \times 6) \, cm^2 = 24 \div 2$
$= 12 \, cm^2$
b $A = \frac{1}{2}(8 \times 5) \, cm^2 = 40 \div 2$
$= 20 \, cm^2$
c $A = \frac{1}{2}(5 \times 7) \, cm^2 = 35 \div 2$
$= 17 \cdot 5 \, cm^2$
d $A = \frac{1}{2}(9 \times 8) \, cm^2 = 72 \div 2$
$= 36 \, cm^2$
e $A = \frac{1}{2}(6 \times 12) \, cm^2 = 72 \div 2$
$= 36 \, cm^2$
f $A = \frac{1}{2}(10 \times 9) \, cm^2 = 90 \div 2$
$= 45 \, cm^2$

3 a
b A: $A = 6 \times 3 = 18 \, cm^2$
B: $A = 4 \times 2 = 8 \, cm^2$

C: $A = 6 \times 4 = 24\,cm^2$
or $8 \times 3 = 24\,cm^2$
D: $A = 4·5 \times 4 = 18\,cm^2$
or $9 \times 2 = 18\,cm^2$
E: $A = 5 \times 3 = 15\,cm^2$
or $2·5 \times 6 = 15\,cm^2$

? Any △ can be made into a rectangle but those that are not right-angled require 2 cuts to produce 2 small right-angled triangles that can be rotated separately to form the rectangle.

PB ■ 70

1 a A and H
C and L
D and N
E and O
F and J
G and I
K and M
B is the odd one out.
b Child's drawing of a kite identical to shape B
c Child's drawing of identical isosceles trapeziums
d Shapes with parallel lines: C, D, E, F, G, I, J, L, N, O
e Shapes with perpendicular lines: D, F, G, I, J, N

2 A = parallelograms
B = rectangles
C = square
D = oblong
E = rhombus
F = (non-special) parallelogram
G = trapezium
H = (non-special) quadrilateral
I = arrowhead
J = kite

PB ■ 71

1 To translate shape A:
● to position B
add **4** units to the x-coordinates
and **0** units to the y-coordinates
● to position C
add **0** units to the x-coordinates
and **4** units to the y-coordinates
● to position D
add **4** units to the x-coordinates
and **4** units to the y-coordinates

2 To A: translate 2 units to the left
To B: translate 2 units to the right
To C: translate 1 unit to the left and 2 units up
To D: translate 1 unit to the left and 2 units down
To E: translate 1 unit to the right and 2 units up
To F: translate 1 unit to the right and 2 units down

3 To A: translate 3 units to the left and 1 unit up
To B: translate 3 units to the right and 1 unit down
To C: translate 1 unit to the left and 3 units up
To D: translate 2 unit to the left and 2 units down
To E: translate 2 unit to the right and 2 units up
To F: translate 1 unit to the right and 3 units down

4 a 5 possible translations
b 11 possible translations

? Child's own translated triangles to show that the larger the triangle the fewer the translations possible in a grid of given size.

PB ■ 72

1

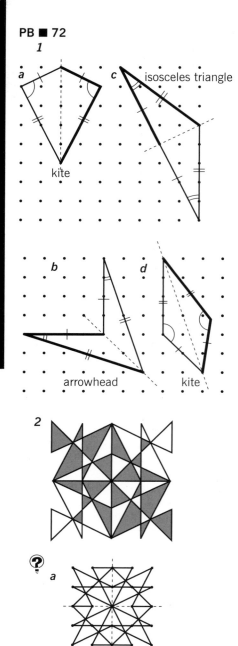

a

c isosceles triangle

kite

b

d

arrowhead   kite

b

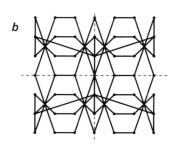

2

a

PB ■ 73

1

a

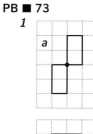

b

c

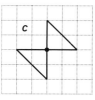

d

e

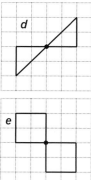

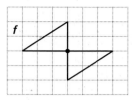

f

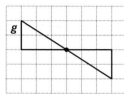

g

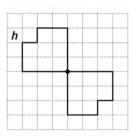

h

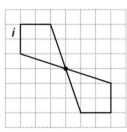

i

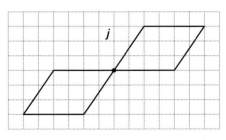

j

2

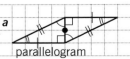

a

parallelogram

b

rectangle

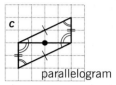

c

parallelogram

d

square

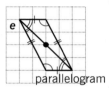

e

parallelogram

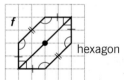

f

hexagon

a

b

c

d

e

f

PB ■ 74

1 a Front:

G
R

Side:

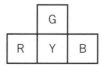

	G	
R	Y	B

Top:

R	G	B

b Front:

G	
B	Y

Side:

G	R
B	Y

Top:

G	R
	Y

c Front:

Y	
R	G
B	G

Side:

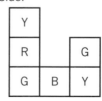

Y		
R		G
G	B	Y

Top:

Y		
G	B	G

d Front:

Side:

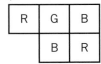

Top:

R	G	B
	B	R

2 Child's constructed shape:

3 a Maximum number of cubes to make the shape: 29
  b Child's drawing to show cubes used.

Minimum number of cubes to make the shape: 25.

PB ■ 75

1 Child's constructed shape.

2 a The new shape is like two regular tetrahedra 'passing through' each other, one inverted compared to the other.
  b The shape has 14 vertices, 36 edges and 24 faces.

Other shapes made from tetrahedra include:
dodecahedron from 4 equal sized tetrahedra, 1 attached to each face of a further equal sized tetrahedron.

PB ■ 76

1 a–b Child's constructed pyramids
  c Shapes that can be made by putting 2 pyramids face to face include: octahedron – from putting the square faces together.

2 a Child's constructed box
  b The box is a **triangular** prism. It has **5** faces, **9** edges and **6** vertices.

The following are also nets for a square based pyramid:

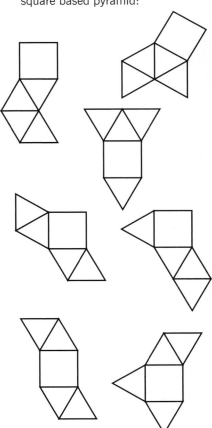

PB ■ 77

1 *a* 128
   b 28
   c 200
   d 90
   e 216
   f 81
   g 128
   h 96
   i 128
   j 162

2 *a* 64
   b 72
   c–d

starting square	square cut out of corners	box dimensions	number of cubes
10 × 10	1 × 1	8 × 8 × 1	64
10 × 10	2 × 2	6 × 6 × 2	72
10 × 10	3 × 3	4 × 4 × 3	48
10 × 10	4 × 4	2 × 2 × 4	16

starting square	square cut out of corners	box dimensions	number of cubes
11 × 11	1 × 1	9 × 9 × 1	81
11 × 11	2 × 2	7 × 7 × 2	98
11 × 11	3 × 3	5 × 5 × 3	75
11 × 11	4 × 4	3 × 3 × 4	36
11 × 11	5 × 5	1 × 1 × 5	5

PB ■ 78

1 *a* ∠BAD, ∠CAD, ∠ADC
   b ∠BCA, ∠BCD, ∠ACD

2 *a* ∠DBE = 90°
     ∠DBC = 35°
     ∠EBC = 125°

   b ∠SQR = 140°
     ∠QSP = 70°
     ∠SPQ = 70°

3 ∠EBH = 90°

4 *a–b* Child's own diagrams and explanations to show that all 4 statements are true

PB ■ 79

1 *a*

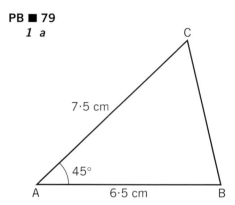

  b

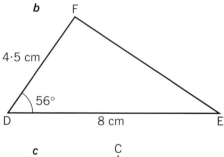

  c

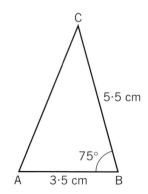

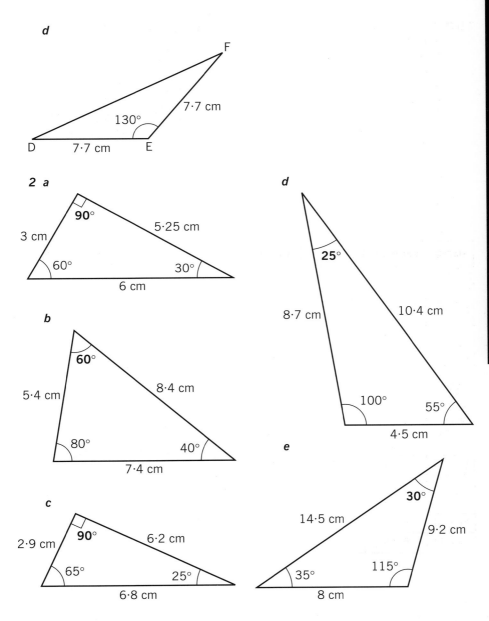

d

F

7·7 cm

130°

D   7·7 cm   E

2 a

90°

3 cm

5·25 cm

60°   30°

6 cm

b

60°

5·4 cm

8·4 cm

80°   40°

7·4 cm

c

90°

2·9 cm   6·2 cm

65°   25°

6·8 cm

d

25°

8·7 cm   10·4 cm

100°   55°

4·5 cm

e

30°

14·5 cm   9·2 cm

35°   115°

8 cm

f

18°

17·4 cm

15·3 cm

57° 105°

5·2 cm

PB ■ 80

1 a $\angle A = 90°$
   $\angle B = 60°$
   $\angle C = 120°$

b Angles around a point total 360°
   so where *n* equal angles meet at a
   point, each angle is $360° \div n$.

2 a $\angle A = 60°$
   $\angle B = 120°$
   $\angle C = 60°$
   $\angle D = 90°$
   $\angle E = 120°$
   $\angle F = 60°$
   $\angle G = 120°$
   $\angle H = 60°$

b $\angle A$, $\angle C$, $\angle F$ and $\angle H$ are all
   angles of equilateral triangles,
   which have 3 equal angles.
   Angles of a triangle add up to
   $180° \therefore \angle A$, $\angle C$, $\angle F$ and
   $\angle H = 180° \div 3 = 60°$

Angles at a point add up to
$360° \therefore \angle B = (360° - 60° - 60°)$
$\div 2 = 240° \div 2 = 120°$
$\angle D$ is an angle of a square.
$\angle E$ and $\angle G$ are angles of a
regular hexagon so $\angle E = \angle G = \angle B$
(or $\angle E = 360° - 60° - 60° - 60°$
$- 60° = 120°$ and
$\angle G = 360° - 60° - 90° - 90°$
$= 120°$).

3 a $\angle A = 36°$
   $\angle B = 45°$
   $\angle C = 112·5°$
   $\angle D = 45°$
   $\angle E = 135°$
   $\angle F = 135°$
b $\angle A = 360° - (3 \times 108°)$
   $= 360° - 324° = 36°$
   $\angle B = 360° \div 8 = 45°$
   $\angle C = (360° - 45° - 90°) \div 2$
   $= 112·5°$
   $\angle D = 360° \div 8 = 45°$
   $\angle E = (360° - 90°) \div 2 = 135°$
   $\angle F = (360° - 90°) \div 2 = 135°$

PB ■ 81
1 a

Length of shadow	Height of pyramid
50 m	**25 m**
356 m	178 m
137 m	**68·5 m**
418 m	209 m
67·5 m	**33·75 m**
770 m	385 m

2 12 m

3 6 m

PB ■ 82

1 **a** likely/unlikely depending on local conditions
b impossible
c unlikely
d likely/unlikely depending upon child
e likely
f likely/unlikely depending upon child
Game
If you know which cards have already been turned over you can use that information to make a prediction that is more likely to be correct.

(?) If the game is played with 2 or more suits, then the rules have to be adapted to allow for the possibility that the number could be the same. This does affect the probabilities.

PB ■ 83

1 Probability scale with the following probabilities marked:
a $\frac{1}{10}$
b $\frac{5}{10}$
c $\frac{6}{10}$
d $\frac{8}{10}$
e $\frac{2}{10}$

2 **a–b** Child's own answers depending on classroom situation.

PB ■ 84

1 **a** $100 + 101 = 201$
$100 + 102 = 202$
$100 + 103 = 203$
$100 + 104 = 204$
$101 + 102 = 203$
$101 + 103 = 204$
$101 + 104 = 205$
$102 + 103 = 205$
$102 + 104 = 206$
$103 + 104 = 207$
b Some answers occur more frequently than others because the numbers are consecutive with values spread equally around the middle value.
c 201: probability $= 0\cdot1$
202: probability $= 0\cdot1$
203: probability $= 0\cdot2$
204: probability $= 0\cdot2$
205: probability $= 0\cdot2$
206: probability $= 0\cdot1$
207: probability $= 0\cdot1$

2 **a** $0\cdot2$
b 6 times
c–d Child's record of results from own investigation and explanation of findings.

(?) If 2 names are picked each time, theoretical probability of any one name being picked is $0\cdot4$. You would expect each name to appear 12 times.
If 3 names are picked each time, theoretical probability of any one name being picked is $0\cdot6$. You would expect each name to appear 18 times.
If 4 names are picked each time, theoretical probability of any one name being picked is $0\cdot8$. You would expect each name to appear 24 times.
If 5 names are picked each time, theoretical probability of any one name being picked is 1. You would expect each name to appear 30 times.

PB ■ 85

1 **a** $0\cdot10$
b $0\cdot40$

c 0·55
d 0·73
e 0·90
f 0·68
g 0·13
h 0·08

2 Results of child's investigation and record of experimental probabilities.

PB ■ 86
Results of child's individual investigations.

PB ■ 87
Results of child's individual investigations.

PB ■ 88

1 a 1–30, 31–60, 61–90, 91–120, 121–150
b 1–20, 21–40, 41–60, 61–80, 81–100
c 1–12, 13–24, 25–36, 37–48, 49–60
d 1–50, 51–100, 101–150, 151–200, 201–250
e 300–309, 310–319, 320–329, 330–339, 340–349
f 0–4, 5–9, 10–14, 15–19, 20–24

2 *a*

Test score	Frequency
1–5	0
6–10	3
11–15	5
16–20	9
21–25	3
26–30	10

b The data show that two thirds of the children scored over half while a third of them did very well, scoring 26–30 marks. No child scored less than 6.

c One possible answer is:

Test score	Frequency
1–10	3
11–20	14
21–30	13

d One possible answer is:

Test score	Frequency
0–2	0
3–5	0
6–8	1
9–11	2
12–14	4
15–17	3
18–20	7
21–23	2
24–26	3
27–29	5
30–32	3

3 a Child's investigation of class sizes. Many schools will not have enough classes to make grouping the numbers a worthwhile exercise.

b Child's own answer.

PB ■ 89
1 a–d Child's own estimates.

2 Child's own investigation.

PB ■ 90
1 a 50%
 b 12·5%

c 75%
d 10%
e 20%
f 60%
g 80%
h 37·5%

2 a Approximate proportions and numbers:

Turkey burger	$\frac{1}{4}$	45
Meatballs	$\frac{1}{8}$	22 or 23
Cheesy pizza	$\frac{5}{8}$	113 or 112
Baked beans	$\frac{1}{2}$	90
Potato wedges	$\frac{1}{4}$	45
Slice of bread	$\frac{3}{20}$	27
Salad	$\frac{1}{10}$	18

b

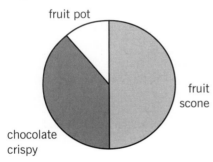

fruit pot

fruit scone

chocolate crispy

3 Child's own comment.

PB ■ 91

1 a median = 38
  range = 72
 b median = 261·5
  range = 10
 c median = £30
  range = £30
 d median = 5
  range = 6·3
 e median = 73·5
  range = 54
 f median = 21
  range = 206

2 a–d Results and report of child's investigation.

PB ■ 92

Results, statistics and report from child's investigation.

ACTIVITY SHEETS

AS ■ 1

1 a 5·8
  b 6·35
  c 6·9
  d 7·28
  e 7·72

2 a 430 g 0·44 kg 4 kg
  b 0·3 l 0·32 l 360 ml
  c £0·78 87p £1·07
  d 7·59 °C 7·6 °C 7·63 °C

AS ■ 2

1 a 3 kg
  b 4 kg
  c 5 kg

2 a Any number n: $4{\cdot}75 \leqslant n < 4{\cdot}85$,
    e.g. 4·75 4·81 4·849
  b Any number n: $7{\cdot}95 \leqslant n < 8{\cdot}05$,
    e.g. 7·95 8·02 8·045

3 Any number with 2 decimal places, n:
$14{\cdot}5 \leqslant n < 15{\cdot}5$, e.g. 15·46 seconds
$22{\cdot}5 \leqslant n < 23{\cdot}5$, e.g. 22·53 m
$21{\cdot}5 \leqslant n < 22{\cdot}5$, e.g. 22·02 seconds
$3{\cdot}5 \leqslant n < 4{\cdot}5$, e.g. 3·89 m
$35{\cdot}5 \leqslant n < 36{\cdot}5$, e.g. 36·39 seconds

4 Child's own answers. C ÷ D rounded
to the nearest tenth should produce
answers around 3 (an approximation
to pi (π)).

AS ■ 3

1 a 32 12 17 ⁻3 2 **⁻18**
    ⁻13 **⁻33** **⁻28**
  b 16 9 7 0 ⁻2 **⁻9** **⁻11**
    ⁻18 **⁻20**
  c 12 20 5 13 ⁻2 **6** **⁻9**
    ⁻1 **⁻16**

2

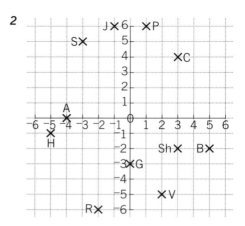

? Child's own objects marked on map
with coordinates noted.

AS ■ 4

1 a Possible answers include:
    $0 - 4 = {}^-4, {}^-2 - 2 = {}^-4,$
    $21 - 25 = {}^-4$
  b Possible answers include:
    ${}^-1 - 8 = {}^-9, 24 - 33 = {}^-9,$
    ${}^-11 + 2 = {}^-9$
  c Possible answers include:
    ${}^-24 + 1 = {}^-23,$
    $77 - 100 = {}^-23, {}^-13 - 10 = {}^-23$

2 a

⁻3	⁻2	2
4	⁻1	⁻6
⁻4	0	1

  b

4	⁻1	12
13	5	⁻3
⁻2	11	6

  c

5	⁻10	17
16	4	⁻8
⁻9	18	3

d

0·5	⁻2	1·5
1	0	⁻1
⁻1·5	2	⁻0·5

3 Adding 3 'sign' numbers to make zero: 12, ⁻9, ⁻3; 12, ⁻8, ⁻4; 11, ⁻9, ⁻2; 11, ⁻8, ⁻3; 11, ⁻7, ⁻4; 5, ⁻3, ⁻2

Adding 4 'sign' numbers to make zero: 12, ⁻7, ⁻3, ⁻2;
12, ⁻6, ⁻4, ⁻2; 11, ⁻6, ⁻3, ⁻2;
12, 5, ⁻9, ⁻8; 11, 5, ⁻9, ⁻7

Adding 5 'sign' numbers to make zero: all answers to 4 'sign' numbers +0; 12, 11, ⁻9, ⁻8, ⁻6; 12, 5, ⁻7, ⁻6, ⁻4; 11, 5, ⁻7, ⁻6, ⁻3

Possible answers include:
⁻8 − ⁻6 − ⁻2 = 0;
12 − 11 + ⁻3 − ⁻2 = 0;
⁻9 + ⁻7 + ⁻2 + 12 − ⁻6 = 0

AS ■ 5

1 a

Positive whole number	Value
N(1)	1
N(2)	2
N(3)	3
N(4)	4
N(5)	5
N(6)	6
N(7)	7
N(8)	8
N(9)	9
N(10)	10
N(n)	n

b

Even number	Value
E(1)	2
E(2)	4
E(3)	6
E(4)	8
E(5)	10
E(6)	12
E(7)	14
E(8)	16
E(9)	18
E(10)	20
E(n)	$2n$

c

Odd number	Value
O(1)	1
O(2)	3
O(3)	5
O(4)	7
O(5)	9
O(6)	11
O(7)	13
O(8)	15
O(9)	17
O(10)	19
O(n)	$2n - 1$

2 a O(1) + 1 = 2 = E(1)
O(1) + 1 = 4 = E(2)
O(**3**) + 1 = **6** = E(**3**)
O(**4**) + 1 = **8** = E(**4**)
O(n) + 1 = $2n$ = E(n)

b $\frac{1}{2}E(1) = 1 = N(1)$
$\frac{1}{2}E(2) = 2 = N(2)$
$\frac{1}{2}E(\mathbf{3}) = \mathbf{3} = N(\mathbf{3})$
$\frac{1}{2}E(\mathbf{4}) = \mathbf{4} = N(\mathbf{4})$
$\frac{1}{2}E(n) = \mathbf{n} = N(n)$

c $2N(1) - 1 = 1 = O(1)$
$2N(1) - 1 = 3 = O(2)$
$2N(\mathbf{3}) - 1 = \mathbf{5} = O(\mathbf{3})$
$2N(\mathbf{4}) - 1 = \mathbf{7} = O(\mathbf{4})$
$2N(n) - 1 = \mathbf{2n - 1} = O(n)$

3 $O(1) + O(2) + O(3) + O(4) + O(5)$
$= 1 + 3 + 5 + 7 + 9$
$= 25$
$= 5^2$

$O(1) + O(2) + O(3) + O(4) + O(5)$
$+ O(6) = 1 + 3 + 5 + 7 + 9 + 11$
$= 36$
$= 6^2 \dots$
$O(1) + O(2) + \dots + O(n)$
$= 1 + 3 + \dots + 2n - 1 = n^2$

(?)

	n	n^2
$E(1) + E(2) = 2 + 4 = \mathbf{6}$	**2**	**4**
$E(1) + E(2) + E(3)$		
$= 2 + 4 + 6$		
$= \mathbf{12}$	**3**	**9**
$E(1) + E(2) + E(3) + E(4)$		
$= 2 + 4 + 6 + 8$		
$= \mathbf{20}$	**4**	**16**
$E(1) + E(2) + E(3) + E(4) + E(5)$		
$= 2 + 4 + 6 + 8 + 10$		
$= \mathbf{30}$	**5**	**25**
$E(1) + E(2) + E(3) + E(4)$		
$+ E(5) + E(6)$		
$= 2 + 4 + 6 + 8 + 10 + 12$		
$= \mathbf{42}$	**6**	**36**

The sum of the first n even numbers
is $n^2 + n$.

1 a

Triangular number	Differences
1	
3	2
6	3
10	4
15	5
21	6
28	7
36	8

b Triangular numbers follow the pattern of odd, odd, even, even, ...

c The differences are the sequence of natural (or counting) numbers.

2 a Number of dominoes:
1 3 **6 10 15 21 28**

b The number of dominoes follows the pattern of triangular numbers.

3

a   **b**   **c**   **d**

1 line   3 lines   6 lines   10 lines

1 a 2, 2
b 4, 4
c 6, 6
d $2\frac{1}{3}$, $2\frac{1}{3}$
e $4\frac{4}{5}$, $4\frac{4}{5}$
f $4\frac{1}{2}$, $4\frac{1}{2}$

2 a 8
b 15
c 12
d 10
e 6
f 14

3 a 35
b 33
c 20

ACTIVITY SHEETS

d 84
e 60
f 100

AS ■ 8

1

Proportion	Fraction	Decimal	Percentage
1 in every 2	$\frac{1}{2}$	0·5	50%
3 in every 10	$\frac{3}{10}$	0·3	30%
4 in every 10 (2 in every 5)	$\frac{4}{10} = \frac{2}{5}$	0·4	40%
16 in every 100 (4 in every 25)	$\frac{16}{100} = \frac{4}{25}$	0·16	16%
5 in every 40	$\frac{5}{40} = \frac{1}{8}$	0·125	12·5%

2

Fibre	Percentage	Decimal	Fraction
wool	70%	0·7	$\frac{7}{10}$
nylon	15%	0·15	$\frac{15}{100} = \frac{3}{20}$
polyester	10%	0·1	$\frac{1}{10}$
other fibres	5%	0·05	$\frac{5}{100} = \frac{1}{20}$

3

Proportion of dominoes	Fraction	Decimal (to 2 decimal places)	Percentage (to nearest whole number)
that are doubles	$\frac{7}{28} = \frac{1}{4}$	0·25	25%
with at least 1 odd number	$\frac{18}{28} = \frac{9}{14}$	0·64	64%
whose sum is an even number	$\frac{16}{28} = \frac{4}{7}$	0·57	57%
whose difference is a prime number	$\frac{11}{28}$	0·39	39%

Note 1 is not a prime number.

AS ■ 9

1 *a* Possible answers include:
   2 : 6, 3 : 9, 4 : 12, 5 : 15 ...
   b Possible answers include:
   10 : 4, 15 : 6, 20 : 8, 25 : 10 ...

2 Possible answers in include:

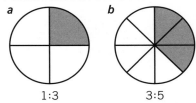

1:3   3:5

Shaded areas are red.
Unshaded areas are green.

3

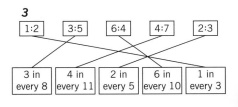

Sets of dominoes	Ratio of odd to even totals (in simplest form)	Proportion of odd totals (in simplest form)	Proportion of even totals (in simplest form)
1s and blanks	1 : 2	1 in every 3	2 in every 3
2s, 1s and blanks	1 : 2	1 in every 3	2 in every 3
3s, 2s, 1s and blanks	2 : 3	2 in every 5	3 in every 5
4s, 3s, 2s, 1s and blanks	2 : 3	2 in every 5	3 in every 5
5s, 4s, 3s, 2s, 1s and blanks	3 : 4	3 in every 7	4 in every 7
6s, 5s, 4s, 3s, 2s, 1s and blanks	3 : 4	3 in every 7	4 in every 7

AS ■ 10

1 Possible answers include:

$(4 \times 5 + 3 - 1) \times (6 + 2)$
$= 22 \times 8 = 176$
$(4 \times 5) + (3 - 1 \times 6 + 2)$
$= 20 + {}^-1 = 19$
$(4 \times 5 + 3) - (1 \times 6 + 2)$
$= 23 - 8 = 15$
$4 \times (5 + 3 - 1) \times (6 + 2)$
$= 4 \times 7 \times 8 = 224$
$(4 \times 5) + (3 - 1) \times 6 + 2$
$= 20 + 2 \times 6 + 2 = 34$
$4 \times (5 + 3) - (1 \times 6) + 2$
$= 4 \times 8 - 6 + 2 = 28$
$4 \times (5 + 3) - 1 \times (6 + 2)$
$= 4 \times 8 - 1 \times 8 = 24$
$4 \times 5 + (3 - 1) \times (6 + 2)$
$= 20 + 2 \times 8 = 36$
$((4 \times 5 + 3 - 1) \times 6) + 2$
$= 22 \times 6 + 2 = 134$

2 $(13 + 2) \times (13 - 2)$
$= 15 \times 11 = 165$

3 Possible answers include:

a $456 = 75 \times 6 + 10 - 4$
b $361 = 75 \times 4 + 10 \times 6 + 1$
c $757 = 75 \times 10 + 6 + 1$
d $397 = 75 \times 4 + 10 \times 9 + 6 + 1$

AS ■ 11

1 a $3 \times 11 = 33$
b $4 \times 9 = 36$
c $6 \times 7 = 42$
d $6 \times 9 = 54$
e $8 \times 7 = 56$
f $7 \times 9 = 63$

2 a $12 \times 4\frac{1}{2}$
   $6 \times 9 = 54$
b $14 \times 2\frac{1}{2}$
   $7 \times 5 = 35$
c $18 \times 6\frac{1}{2}$
   $9 \times 13 = 117$
d $16 \times 2\frac{1}{4}$
   $8 \times 4\frac{1}{2}$
   $4 \times 9 = 36$
e $12 \times 4\frac{1}{4}$
   $6 \times 8\frac{1}{2}$
   $3 \times 17 = 51$
f $24 \times 6\frac{1}{4}$
   $12 \times 12\frac{1}{2}$
   $6 \times 25 = 150$

AS ■ 12

1 a 60
b 82
c 94
d 106
e 126
f 148

2 a 0·52
b 0·49
c 0·22
d 0·33
e 0·06
f 0·92

3 $50 = {}^-2 + 52$ $50 = {}^-3 + 53$
  $50 = {}^-4 + 54$ $50 = {}^-6 + 56$
  $50 = {}^-7 + 57$ $50 = {}^-8 + 58$

4 a $^-13$
b $^-22$
c $^-29$
d $^-34$
e $^-41$
f $^-49$

5 28, 72; 29, 71; 30, 70; 31, 69;
  32, 68; 38, 62; 39, 61; 40, 60;
  41, 59; 42, 58; 48, 52; 49, 51

AS ■ 13

1 a

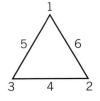
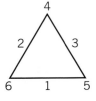

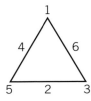
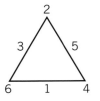

b The numbers in each corner form
a sequence with a constant
difference, e.g. 1, 2, 3; 2, 4, 6.

c Possible rules include:
Choose a sequence of the
numbers with a constant
difference to put at the corners.

Put the smallest of the remaining
numbers between the pair of numbers
with the biggest sum, the largest of the
remaining numbers between the pair of
numbers with the smallest sum, ...

? The above rules apply to a set of
consecutive numbers. The set 0–5
behaves in the same way, as does
a set of consecutive even numbers.
Suggest that children begin their
exploration of a random set of
numbers by choosing the corner
numbers from a sequence with a
constant difference, e.g. 2, 5, 8
and then finding 'middle' numbers
that fit, e.g. 9, 3, 6 or 11, 5, 8 ...
When they have sets of 6 numbers
that form magic triangles, they
can then investigate whether there
are always four solutions (this is
not so if any of the numbers are
repeated as in 2, 5, 5, 8, 8, 11).
Children should then choose totally
random sets of 6 numbers and try
to find solutions, pooling their
examples and ideas before coming
to some conclusions about what
conditions they think must apply
to make a magic triangle
possible.

AS ■ 14

1 a

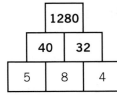

b

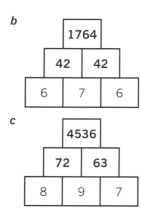

c

2 Possible answers include:

a

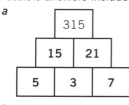

b

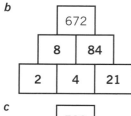

c

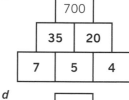

d

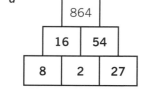

3 a

Birthday	Amount given to Dylan
1st	£1
2nd	£2
3rd	£4
4th	£8
5th	£16
6th	£32
7th	£64
8th	£128
9th	£256
10th	£512

b £1023

c Dylan first receives more than £1 million (£1 048 576) on his 21st birthday.

AS ■ 15

1 a
$$\begin{array}{r} 1\,5\,7\,7\,6 \\ +\,7\,4\,6\,3\,9 \\ \hline 9\,0\,4\,1\,5 \end{array}$$

b
$$\begin{array}{r} 5\,6\,2\,0\,6 \\ +\,3\,9\,0\,9\,7 \\ \hline 9\,5\,3\,0\,3 \end{array}$$

c
$$\begin{array}{r} 6\,4\,7\,1\,8 \\ +\,2\,8\,7\,0\,2 \\ \hline 9\,3\,4\,2\,0 \end{array}$$

d
$$\begin{array}{r} 2\,4\cdot 7\,2 \\ +\,\,\,7\cdot 3\,9 \\ \hline 3\,2\cdot 1\,1 \end{array}$$

e
$$\begin{array}{r} 3\,1\cdot 0\,6 \\ +\,4\,9\cdot 3\,8 \\ \hline 8\,0\cdot 4\,4 \end{array}$$

f
$$\begin{array}{r} 5\,2\cdot 4\,7 \\ +\,3\,6\cdot 5\,6 \\ \hline 8\,9\cdot 0\,3 \end{array}$$

2 Child's own answers.

AS ■ 16

1 a 45 876 WATCH
 b 90 876 DITCH
 c 401 629 WISHED
 d 307 218 NICEST

2 Child's own subtraction questions
giving the answers:
76 538   82 576   324 218
7 658 829.

3 8428

🔮 Child's own 'secret number'
question.

AS ■ 17

1 a B = 3, C = 1, D = 6
 b B = 6, C = 3, D = 7
 c B = 0, C = 7, D = 3
 d B = 2, C = 0, D = 5

2 a −, −, +
 b −, −, −, −, +, −
 c +, +, +, −, +
 d −, +, +, −
 e +, −, −, +

3 Child's own answers. The first and
last numbers should be the same.

🔮 If the starting number is even the
last number will still be the same.

AS ■ 18

1 a $2 \cdot 4 \times 10 \times 2$ $24 \times 2 = 48$
 b $4 \cdot 2 \times 10 \times 3$ $42 \times 3 = 126$
 c $3 \cdot 1 \times 10 \times 4$ $31 \times 4 = 124$
 d $2 \cdot 3 \times 10 \times 3$ $23 \times 3 = 69$
 e $4 \cdot 3 \times 10 \times 4$ $43 \times 4 = 172$

2 a $132 \div 2$ $66 \div 3 = 22$
 b $186 \div 2$ $93 \div 3 = 31$
 c $168 \div 2$ $84 \div 4 = 21$
 d $280 \div 4$ $70 \div 2 = 35$
 e $162 \div 3$ $54 \div 3 = 18$

3 One solution is:
$139\,230 = 13\,923 \times 10$
$= 4641 \times 30 = 1547 \times 90$
$= 221 \times 630$
Others are: 315×442; 170×759

🔮 18×7735, 30×4641,
 42×3315, 70×1989,
 90×1547, 45×3094,
 63×2210

AS ■ 19

1 a
```
      358
    × 67
    21480
     2506
    23986
```

 b
```
      457
    × 68
    27420
     3656
    31076
```

 c
```
      956
    × 69
    57360
     8604
    65964
```

2 a 4
 b 6
 c 9
 d 6
 e 8
 f 7

3 $859 \times 76 = 65\,284$

AS ■ 20

1 Numbers coloured:
163, 187, 195, 203, 219, 227, 259, 267, 291, 339, 379, 427

2

Division	Whole number and remainder	Mixed number	Decimal to 2 decimal places
19 ÷ 4	4 r 3	$4\frac{3}{4}$	4·75
87 ÷ 4	21 r 3	$21\frac{3}{4}$	21·75
73 ÷ 6	12 r 1	$12\frac{1}{6}$	12·17
91 ÷ 6	15 r 1	$15\frac{1}{6}$	15·17
117 ÷ 6	19 r 3	$19\frac{1}{2}$	19·50
121 ÷ 8	15 r 1	$15\frac{1}{8}$	15·13
137 ÷ 8	17 r 1	$17\frac{1}{8}$	17·13
149 ÷ 8	18 r 5	$18\frac{5}{8}$	18·63

3 Possible answers include:
59 ÷ 3, 118 ÷ 6, 590 ÷ 30

4 a $15\frac{3}{4}$ $12\frac{5}{8}$

b Possible answers include: 41, 83, 125, 167 ...

c Possible answers include: 13, 85, 157, 229 ...

AS ■ 21

1 a Possible approximation:
700 ÷ 20 = 35

```
  2 3)7 3 6
   −6 9 0      30 × 23
      4 6
    −4 6       2 × 23
       0       Answer: 32
```

b Possible approximation:
900 ÷ 30 = 30

```
  2 9)8 9 9
   −8 7 0      30 × 29
      2 9
    −2 9       1 × 29
       0       Answer: 31
```

c Possible approximation:
990 ÷ 30 = 33

```
  3 1)9 9 2
   −9 3 0      30 × 31
      6 2
    −6 2       2 × 31
       0       Answer: 32
```

d Possible approximation:
900 ÷ 50 = 18

```
  4 7)8 9 3
   −4 7 0      10 × 47
      4 2 3
    −4 2 3     9 × 47
         0     Answer: 19
```

2 Coloured pairs: 3129, 6; 4027, 8; 1768, 4; 4796, 9; 2672, 5; 3432, 7.

AS ■ 22

AS ■ 23

1 Possible answers include:
a 828 ÷ 4 =, 820 ÷ 4 + 2 =
b 1420 ÷ 4 =, 2840 ÷ 8 =

2 a&b Each problem matched to the most likely answer with child's own reason.

c Exact answers:
£4·56 £5·88 £6·84 £5·46
Correct decisions ticked.

AS ■ 24

1
  a 327
  b 351
  c 40
  d 612
  e 20
  f 310

2 Paid out: **£1170·54**
Balance: £9342·56 £9192·82
£9601·07 **£8882·01** **£6350·03**
£8152·85 £6982·31 **£7022·62**
£7073·71 **£5237·69** **£9999·99**

3 Possible answers include:
  a $95 \div 5$
  b $(9 + 5) \times 6$
  c $9 - (8 - 6)$
  d $9 \times 5 - 6$
  e $5 \times 5 + 8$
  f $96 + 5$

AS ■ 25

1
  a 7
  b 4
  c 6
  d 9
  e 11
  f 12

2
  a 44·75
    Possible answers include:
    $179 \div 4 = 44·75$
    $716 \div 16 = 44·75$
    $89·5 \div 2 = 44·75$
  b $725 \div 6 = 120·83$ to 2 decimal
    places Possible answers include:
    $1450 \div 12 = 120·83$
    $2900 \div 24 = 120·83$
    $7250 \div 60 = 120·83$

AS ■ 26
Time dominoes

AS ■ 27

1
  a Possible estimates include:
    £35 + £2 = £37
    £20 − £5 = £15
    25 × 50p = £12·50
    £60 ÷ 4 = £15
    £27 + £4 + £7 = £38
    £50 − 2 × £12·50 = £25
    £50 − (£5 + £18 + £15 + £3)
      = £9
  b Each problem matched to the
    most likely answer with child's
    own reason.
  c Exact answers: £15·21 £12·69
    £14·86 £38·94 £24·92 £8·63
    Correct decisions ticked.

AS ■ 28

1

x	$x + 1$	$x - 2$	$2x - 1$	$3(x + 2)$	$3x + 2$	$x^2 - 1$	$10 - x$
1	2	⁻1	1	9	5	0	9
7	8	5	13	27	23	48	3
2	3	0	3	12	8	3	8
5	6	3	9	21	17	24	5
9	10	7	17	33	29	80	1
10	11	8	19	36	32	99	0

2

a	b	$a + b$	$a - b$	$2a + 3b$	$a^2 - b$	$a + b^2$	$4(a + 2b)$
1	1	2	0	5	0	2	12
2	1	3	1	7	3	3	16
1	2	3	$^-1$	8	$^-1$	5	20
2	2	4	0	10	2	6	24
3	1	4	2	9	8	4	20
1	3	4	$^-2$	11	$^-2$	10	28
3	2	5	1	12	7	7	28
2	3	5	$^-1$	13	1	11	32

3 Child's own answers

$2a + 2b - 2c =$ twice $(a + b - c)$
$= 2(a + b - c)$

? $3a - 3b + 3c =$ three times $(a - b + c)$
$= 3(a - b + c)$

AS ■ 29

1 **a**

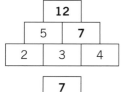

b

b

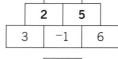

c

c

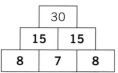

2 Child's own answers.

3 Possible answers include:

a

4 **a**

56

b&c The top number is the sum of the first bottom number and the third bottom number and twice the second bottom number.
If the bottom numbers are a, b, c and t is the top number,
$t = a + 2b + c$

? The top number is the product of the first bottom number, the second bottom number squared and the third bottom number.
If the bottom numbers are a, b, c and t is the top number,
$t = a \times b^2 \times c = ab^2c$

e $3n \quad 3n - 2$
$$3n + 3n - 2 = 46$$
$$6n - 2 = 46$$
$$n = 8$$

2 Child's own answer.

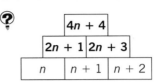

Top number $= 4n + 4 = 4(n + 1) =$ four times the middle bottom number.

AS ■ 30

1 a $n + 19 \quad n + 24$
$$n + 19 + n + 24 = 69$$
$$2n + 43 = 69$$
$$n = 13$$

b $n + 4 \quad n + 9$
$$n + 4 + n + 9 = 45$$
$$2n + 13 = 45$$
$$n = 16$$

c $n + 7 \quad n + 6$
$$n + 7 + n + 6 = 17$$
$$2n + 13 = 17$$
$$n = 2$$

d $n + 14 \quad n + 2n$
$$n + 14 + 3n = 30$$
$$4n + 14 = 30$$
$$n = 4$$

AS ■ 31

1 a OUT: 1   3   5   7   9
b OUT: 8   13   18   23   28

2 a OUT: 17   32   47   62   77
b IN: 17
   OUT: 3   28   53   103
c IN: 2   3   5
   OUT: 2   20

AS ■ 32

1 $n \rightarrow 2n - 1$: $2 \rightarrow 3$, $3 \rightarrow 5$, $10 \rightarrow 19$
$n \rightarrow 2n$: $4 \rightarrow 8$, $10 \rightarrow 20$, $27 \rightarrow 54$
$n \rightarrow 3n + 2$: $4 \rightarrow 14$, $1 \rightarrow 5$

2 Child's own answers.

3 Possible answers include:

Expression	1	2	3
$n + 1 + n + 1$	$n + n + 2$	$2n + 2$	$2(n + 1)$
$2n + 2 + n - 1$	$n + n + 2 + n - 1$	$3n + 2 - 1$	$3n + 1$
$5n - 4n - 4$	$n + n + n + n + n$ $- n - n - n - n - 4$	$n - 4$	$5n - 4(n + 1)$
$3(n + 2)$	$n + 2 + n + 2 + n + 2$	$3n + 3 \times 2$	$3n + 6$

AS ■ 33

1 Possible answers include:

   a 2   2
   b 2   4
   c 2   6
   d 2   8

2

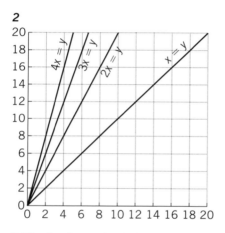

3 The line for each rule is steeper as the multiple of x increases.

b

$x + 6 = y$	
x	**y**
⁻9	⁻3
2	8
0	6
⁻6	0

c

$x - 2 = y$	
x	**y**
2	0
10	8
1	⁻1
⁻8	⁻10

d

$x - 7 = y$	
x	**y**
7	0
10	3
13	6
3	⁻4

AS ■ 34

1 a

$x + 3 = y$	
x	**y**
6	9
7	10
⁻7	⁻4
0	3

2 a&b

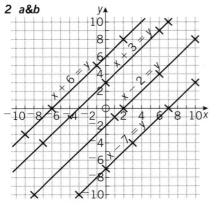

c Each line makes the same angle
with the x-axis.

AS ■ 35

1 a

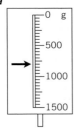

b

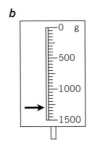

c

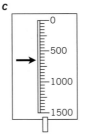

2

Pack	Gross mass	Net mass	Packaging
a	110 g	92 g	18 g
b	**250 g**	181 g	**69 g**
c	**370 g**	337 g	**33 g**
d	**590 g**	**523 g**	67 g
e	**720 g**	**635 g**	85 g
f	**830 g**	**734 g**	96 g
g	**950 g**	**835 g**	115 g

3 a A: 0·75 kg 750 g
   B: 1 kg 1000 g
   C: 1·5 kg 1500g
  b 104 Arran bags
  c 67·5 kg
  d A: 42 bags
    B: 21 bags
    C: 21 bags

AS ■ 36

1 Experimental results should show that the difference in water level is 1 ml for each 1 cm cube.

2

Level of water	ml	cl	Fraction of 1 litre	Percentage	
				full	empty
a	600	60	$\frac{3}{5}$ litre	60%	40%
b	500	50	$\frac{1}{2}$ litre	50%	50%
c	750	75	$\frac{3}{4}$ litre	75%	25%
d	330	33	$\frac{33}{100}$ litre	33%	67%
e	900	90	$\frac{9}{10}$ litre	90%	10%
f	170	17	$\frac{17}{100}$ litre	17%	83%
g	960	96	$\frac{24}{25}$ litre	96%	4%
h	50	5	$\frac{1}{20}$ litre	5%	95%

Note: 330 ml is approximately $\frac{1}{3}$ of 1 litre.

AS ■ 37
World-wide time zones.

AS ■ 38

1 b

Length of side of square pond	Area of water	Outside perimeter
1 m	1 m²	12 m
2 m	4 m²	16 m
3 m	9 m²	20 m
4 m	16 m²	24 m
5 m	25 m²	28 m
6 m	36 m²	32 m

c

Input				Output
length of side of →	+2 →→	×4 →	→	outside perimeter of path
square pond				of path

d

Length of side of square pond	Area of water	Outside perimeter
8 m	64 m²	40 m
10 m	100 m²	48 m
20 m	400 m²	88 m
n m	n^2 m²	$4(n + 2)$ m

AS ■ 39

1 a 1·5 cm²
  b 2 cm²
  c 2·5 cm²
  d 3 cm²
  e 2 cm²
  f 2 cm²
  g 2·5 cm²
  h 2·5 cm²
  i 2·5 cm²
  j 2 cm²
  k 1·5 cm²
  l 1 cm²

2 a 7 cm²
  b 6 cm²
  c 4 cm²
  d 5 cm²

3 Child's own answers.

AS ■ 40

1

Kite	A	B	C	D	E	F
Area in cm²	6	6	5	14	8	18

2 a

Kite	Length in cm		Area in cm²
	Diagonal 1	Diagonal 2	
A	6	2	6
B	4	3	6
C	2	5	5
D	4	7	14
E	4	4	8
F	6	6	18

b $K = \frac{1}{2}(D1 \times D2)$

? 1 cm, 72 cm; 2 cm, 36 cm; 3 cm, 24 cm; 4 cm, 18 cm, 6 cm, 12 cm; 8 cm, 9 cm

AS ■ 41

1

Square	S	T
Area	100 cm²	50 cm²
Length of side to 2 decimal places	10·00 cm	7·07 cm
Perimeter to 2 decimal places	40·00 cm	28·28 cm

2

Square	Area	Length of side to 2 decimal places	Perimeter to 2 decimal places
A	$12 \times 12 = \mathbf{144}$ cm²	$\sqrt{144} = \mathbf{12 \cdot 00}$ cm	$4 \times \sqrt{144} = \mathbf{48 \cdot 00}$ cm
B	$144 \div 2 = \mathbf{72}$ cm²	$\sqrt{72} = \mathbf{8 \cdot 49}$ cm	$4 \times \sqrt{72} = \mathbf{33 \cdot 94}$ cm
C	$\mathbf{72 \div 2 = 36}$ cm²	$\sqrt{36} = \mathbf{6 \cdot 00}$ cm	$4 \times \sqrt{36} = \mathbf{24 \cdot 00}$ cm
D	$\mathbf{36 \div 2 = 18}$ cm²	$\sqrt{18} = \mathbf{4 \cdot 24}$ cm	$4 \times \sqrt{18} = \mathbf{16 \cdot 97}$ cm
E	$\mathbf{18 \div 2 = 9}$ cm²	$\sqrt{9} = \mathbf{3 \cdot 00}$ cm	$4 \times \sqrt{9} = \mathbf{12 \cdot 00}$ cm

(?) Perimeters to 2 decimal places:
F $4 \times \sqrt{4 \cdot 5}$ cm = 8·49 cm;
G $4 \times \sqrt{2 \cdot 25}$ cm = 6·00 cm;
H $4 \times \sqrt{1 \cdot 125}$ cm = 4·24 cm;
I $4 \times \sqrt{0 \cdot 5625}$ cm = 3·00 cm.

AS ■ 42

1 16 cm² 22 cm² 28 cm²
34 cm² 40 cm²

2 a

Length of each edge (cm)	Surface area of each face (cm²)	Total surface area of cube (cm³)
1	1	6
2	4	24
3	9	54
4	16	96
5	25	150
6	36	216

b Predictions for cubes with sides:
8 cm
$(216 + 78 + 90)$ cm² = 384 cm²
10 cm
$(384 + 102 + 114)$ cm² = 600 cm²
12 cm
$(600 + 126 + 138)$ cm² = 864 cm²

ACTIVITY SHEETS

c Surface area of each face of a cube
with sides *n* cm long = n^2 cm^2
Total surface area = 6 n^2 cm^2

Child's own investigation to support
the statement.

_____   _____

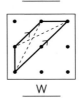

W _____   _____

AS ■ 43

1, 2, 3

V, X

V, X

V, X

Y

Y

Y

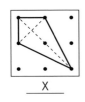

X

X, Z

AS ■ 44

1 a Two out of 7, 9, 11.
b Two out of 6, 8, 12.

2 a 8
b 10
c 4
d 9

3 a&b

b blue
r red
g green
y yellow

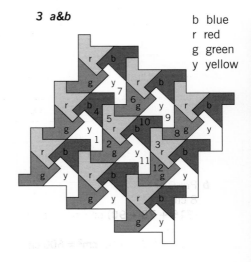

ACTIVITY SHEETS

63

AS ■ 45

1 a

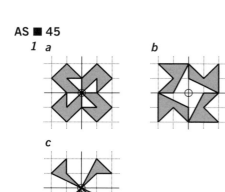

b

c

2 a

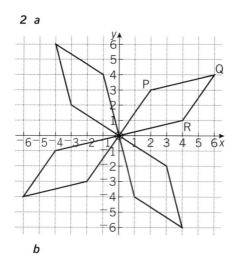

b

Vertex	Quadrant			
	1st	**2nd**	**3rd**	**4th**
P	(2, 3)	(⁻3, 2)	(⁻2, ⁻3)	(3, ⁻2)
Q	(6, 4)	(⁻4, 6)	(⁻6, ⁻4)	(4, ⁻6)
R	(4, 1)	(⁻1, 4)	(⁻4, ⁻1)	(1, ⁻4)

c In the 2nd quadrant the coordinates are reversed and the first coordinate is negative.
In the 3rd quadrant the coordinates are the same as in the 1st quadrant but are both negative.

In the 4th quadrant the coordinates are reversed and the second coordinate is negative.

3 a

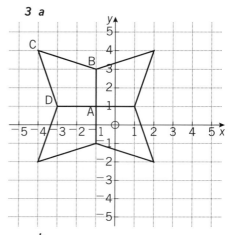

b

Vertex	Quadrant			
	1st	**2nd**	**3rd**	**4th**
C	(2, 4)	(⁻4, 4)	(⁻4, ⁻2)	(2, ⁻2)

AS ■ 46

1 a order 5
b order 6
c order 4
d order 4

2 Possible answers include:

a

b

c

d

3 Children's own answers.

1 a Child's own predicted coordinates.

b

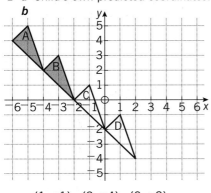

c (1, ⁻1) (2, ⁻4) (0, ⁻2)

2 a Child's own predicted coordinates.

b

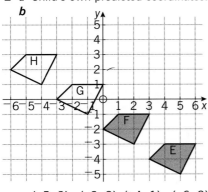

c (⁻5, 3) (⁻3, 3) (⁻4, 1) (⁻6, 2)

3 a

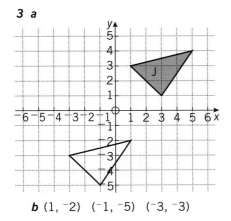

b (1, ⁻2) (⁻1, ⁻5) (⁻3, ⁻3)

4 a

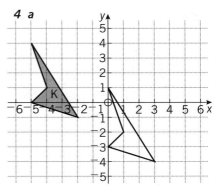

b (0, 1) (3, ⁻4) (0, ⁻3) (1, ⁻2)

AS ■ 48

1 a

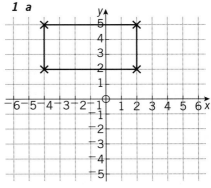

b (⁻4, 2)

2 a

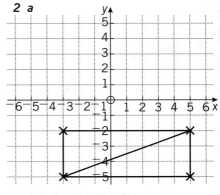

b (⁻3, ⁻2) (5, ⁻5)

65

ACTIVITY SHEETS

3 a

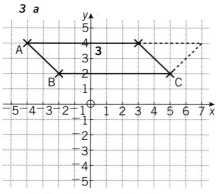

b Parallelogram: (3, 4)
Trapezium: any pair of coordinates
$(n, 4)$ where $n > ^-4$, e.g. (6, 4) or any point on the line $x + y = 7$

AS ■ 49

1

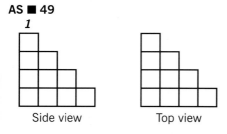

Side view   Top view

2

Number of layers	1	2	3	4	5	6	7	8
Number of cubes	3	4	10	20	35	56	84	120
Difference		3	6	10	15	21	28	36

3 a

Ball numbers	Frequency
$1 \times 2 \times 3 = 6$	$6 \div 6 = 1$
$2 \times 3 \times 4 = 24$	$24 \div 6 = 4$
$3 \times 4 \times 5 = 60$	$60 \div 6 = 10$
$4 \times 5 \times 6 = 120$	$120 \div 6 = 20$
$5 \times 6 \times 7 = 210$	$210 \div 6 = 35$
$6 \times 7 \times 8 = 336$	$336 \div 6 = 56$
$7 \times 8 \times 9 = 504$	$504 \div 6 = 84$
$8 \times 9 \times 10 = 720$	$720 \div 6 = 120$

b The number of cubes follows the sequence 1, 4, 10, 20 … The next number is found by adding the next triangular number. The same sequence can be found by multiplying 3 consecutive numbers beginning with 1 and dividing by 6.

1

Turn	Name of angle	Number of degrees	Turn	Name of angle	Number of degrees
from A to B	AOB	55°	from B to C	**BOC**	**25°**
from A to C	**AOC**	**80°**	from B to D	**BOD**	**90°**
from A to D	**AOD**	**145°**	from B to E	**BOE**	**108°**
from A to E	**AOE**	**164°**	from C to D	**COD**	**66°**
from D to E	**DOE**	**18°**	from C to E	**COE**	**85°**

2 a 270°
 b 294°
 c 342°
 d 196°
 e 275°

3 Child's own answers.

 1 a A, B = 40°
  C, D = 75°
  E, F = 150°
  G, H = 125°
 b equal

 2 a J = 65° K = 115° L = 65°
  M = 115°
 b 180°
 c Child's explanation, e.g. ∠J = ∠K because they are vertically opposite angles where 2 straight lines intersect.

3 a
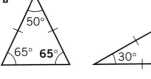
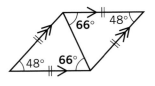

b The base angles of an isosceles triangle are equal.

 1 a 1–6 dice
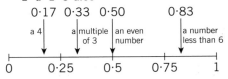

 b 1–8 dice
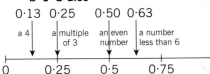

 c 1–10 dice
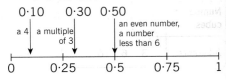

2 a Expected probability is $\frac{1}{4}$ or 0·25 for each number. Child's own answers for experimental probabilities.
 c Child's explanation, e.g. Each time the dice is thrown there is a one in four chance of each number appearing. After a lot of

throws each number will appear about one in four times. This will not always happen for a small number of throws.

AS ■ 53

1 a

Let's play
The game is not fair because the probability of player 1 scoring a point is $\frac{1}{2}$ but the probability of player 2 scoring a point is only $\frac{1}{3}$.

? Possible answers include:
Player 1 scores a point if a head is tossed.
Player 2 scores a point if a number greater than 3 is rolled.
The probability of scoring a point must be equal for player 1 and player 2 if the game is to be fair.

AS ■ 54

1

Outcome	Expected probability		
	square spinner	pentagon spinner	hexagon spinner
1	$\frac{1}{4}$	$\frac{1}{5}$	$\frac{1}{2}$
2	$\frac{1}{4}$	$\frac{2}{5}$	$\frac{1}{3}$
3	$\frac{1}{2}$	$\frac{2}{5}$	$\frac{1}{6}$
an odd number	$\frac{3}{4}$	$\frac{3}{5}$	$\frac{2}{3}$

2 a The numbers that have the greatest probability of being landed on are 3, 3 or 2, and 1 on each spinner respectively, giving a total of 6 or 7. There is a slightly

higher chance of getting 6 as a total, because there are more ways of making 6 than 7.
b&c Child's own answers.
d The estimation should be based on the results in **b&c**, probably close to $\frac{1}{4}$.

AS ■ 55

1 a&b Child's own answers.

2 a Height and shoe size or length of feet for each of a number of people.
b Child's own answer.

? A different conclusion may emerge but 10 people is a small number to ask to get a representative sample and 20 people still do not make a large sample.

AS ■ 56

1 a $\frac{1}{2}$
b $\frac{1}{9}$
c $\frac{2}{3}$
d $\frac{1}{3}$
e $\frac{1}{6}$
f $\frac{1}{18}$
g $\frac{3}{4}$
h $\frac{5}{9}$

2 a

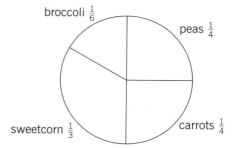

broccoli $\frac{1}{6}$ peas $\frac{1}{4}$ carrots $\frac{1}{4}$ sweetcorn $\frac{1}{3}$

b There would be an extra section showing $\frac{1}{36}$ of the circle for 'broccoli' and 'beans' would be reduced to $\frac{5}{36}$ of the circle.

Child's own survey and pie chart.

Comments may include: the frequency of 1 and 3 on both spinners is about equal; the frequency of 4 and 2 on the second spinner is about twice that of the first; 5 and 6 are not recorded in the second graph.

AS ■ 57

1 a Birds Sam saw between 10:00 and 10:30

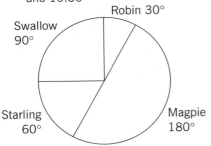

Birds Tom saw between 10:00 and 10:30

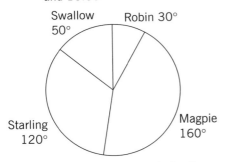

b Possible answers include: the proportion of robins is the same in both charts; the proportion of starlings in Tom's chart is double that in Sam's; neither saw any thrushes.

AS ■ 58

1 a Child's own answers.
b Child's answers based on their results.

2 Possible answers include:

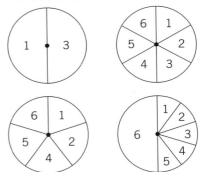

AS ■ 59

1 a 6
b 40
c 34
d 1·5
e 5·5
f 160

2 a–d Child's own answers
e The mean averages show that your heart beats faster (there are more pulses per minute) after exercise.
f The range of data shows how great is the difference between the slowest and fastest heart rates. It may not change after exercise.
g Child's investigation report.

AS ■ 60

1, 2 Child's own answers.